Liquid Gold Ships

—

A History of the Tanker 1859–1984

The Fulmar Floating Storage Unit (FSU) with its shuttle tanker, *Esso Aberdeen*, at its proving trials.

Liquid Gold Ships

A History of the Tanker 1859–1984

by Mike Ratcliffe

LONDON NEW YORK HAMBURG HONG KONG

Lloyd's of London Press Ltd.

1985

Lloyd's of London Press Ltd.
Sheepen Place
Colchester
Essex CO3 3LP
England

USA and CANADA
Lloyd's of London Press Inc.
87 Terminal Drive
Plainview
New York, NY 10003 USA

GERMANY
Lloyd's of London Press
PO Box 11 23 47
Deichstrasse 41
2000 Hamburg 11
West Germany

SOUTH EAST ASIA
Lloyd's of London Press (Far East) Ltd.
1502 Chung Nam Building
1 Lockhart Road
Wanchai
Hong Kong

First published 1985

British Library Cataloguing in Publication Data
Ratcliffe, Mike
Liquid gold ships: a history of the tanker, 1859–1984.
1. Tankers—History
I. Title
623.82′45 VM455
ISBN 0-907432-83-2

Printed in Great Britain by Lavenham Press Ltd.
Water Street, Lavenham, Suffolk

PREFACE

This is the story of the forces that moulded the tanker into what it is today. From the simple oak barrels of 125 years ago when oil was found commercially in the USA, the packaging of petroleum on the high seas has developed into the biggest business in the history of shipping. Tankers have grown so fast in number and size that they account today for some 40% of the total tonnage of world merchant shipping with the largest tankers measuring over half a million tons. This is, therefore, not just a story of how a single new type of specialist ship was born, but of how the largest armada in history has been amassed.

The tanker grew out of the demand to ship oil from the producer to the consumer. So to understand tankers one has to understand the oil industry and with this goes power, politics and money. Unlike the world of oil, where monopolies like that of Rockefeller or oligopolies like that of the "seven sisters" have ruled, the world of tankers has been a totally free market place, where an entrepreneur can one day make a fortune and the next day, just as easily lose it. This environment has attracted many colourful characters who are just as much a part of this story as their ships with their cargo of "liquid gold".

Then there is the other side of the coin: the ship designers and builders who have supplied the hulls and machinery: often tankers have pushed their technology to its limits. A century ago no-one knew how a ship full of an inflammable liquid in the middle of the Atlantic Ocean in the depths of winter would behave; only a decade ago no-one knew what would happen when one built a ship a quarter of a mile long with tanks nearly the size of a cathedral. In both cases disastrous mistakes occurred, resulting in tragic losses. Even so, great strides in design and safety have been made, sometimes in direct response to the ever-changing demand put on tankers, at others due to external forces such as the environmentalist, lobby or politicians.

This book is an attempt to paint the broad but key trends in a highly complex evolution. There have been major watersheds where the industry has drastically changed course. Often this was not apparent at the time and the industry kept going in its old direction for many years before it realised that it had actually changed direction. Much of today's tragic depression and overcapacity is due to this same attitude, for back in the 1970s owners just would not accept that demand for oil, and hence for tankers, was no longer booming in the way it had in the 1960s and kept on ordering new tonnage.

It is all too easy to lose the perspective of history by concentrating on the here and now. I hope that this story will allow many in the tanker industry to regain that perspective and so make better decisions about all our futures.

MIKE RATCLIFFE

CONTENTS

LIST OF ILLUSTRATIONS

*Popperfoto

BOOK I
BIRTH OF AN INDUSTRY
(1859–1900)

The 270,000-deadweight-ton *Texaco Africa,* delivered in 1974. The ship has an overall length of 1,088 feet and capacity for 2,000,000 barrels of crude oil.

1 LIQUID GOLD!

The sight of a super tanker ploughing through the high seas is majestic. Of every thing that man has created nothing is more impressive in sheer size and power than one of these beasts; over a quarter of a mile long, needing nearly 100 feet of water and carrying half a million tons of oil in her belly. It is difficult to conceive that this amount of oil would keep the average motorist's car going for something like 400,000 years, or alternatively 400,000 motorists happy for one year. The tanker and the world she lives in are today ultimate superlatives. If all the tankers in the world were to be added together, they would come to 40% of the total carrying capacity of merchant shipping and if they were all put end to end they would bridge the North Sea from London to Copenhagen, or stretch from New York to Chicago.

This is the story of the creation of this armada of monster ships. But not just the *how*, also the *where* and *when*. To tell it we cannot just look at the world of tankers. Tankers are here to move oil. Oil and the oil industry are therefore the key to our story. To understand why different types and sizes of tankers have been built at certain times, we must follow the forces created within the oil industry. And to appreciate why different nationalities of shipowners have got into tankers and why certain flags have been used, we have to look outside of tankers and at the entire shipping market. Another vital key to the jigsaw is *who* built the tankers. To understand this we have to move beyond shipping and into politics and international finance.

One would not expect the story of the most important transportation vehicle in the world to be simple. The history of tankers certainly is not. It spreads to the four corners of the globe and way back in history, for nearly 150 years in fact. To appreciate the world in which tankers were born we have to forget the comfortable existence we have today, our centrally heated homes and air conditioned offices, our cars and our light bulbs. We have to try to imagine what it was like when there was no instant energy. Back to an era when there was no electricity, no gasoline, no kerosine; back to when most of the world relied on wood to heat the home or fire the kiln; back to the middle of the 19th century.

In 1850, the industrialised world, for what it was worth, was North Europe. America was still a group of agricultural states with thousands of miles untouched even by the settlers: wood supplied over 80% of North America's energy. On the other side of the Atlantic, the industrial revolution was well under way, centred on Britain, the steam engine and coal. Britain had already had her first "energy crisis" back in the 16th century when she had started to run out of wood to burn for fuel and had been forced to turn to coal. This new energy source had made her innovate to find new manufacturing processes so that her infant industries could burn this new fuel efficiently. By the 19th century, she was technologically well ahead of the rest of Europe and far, far in front of the rest of the world.

Victorian Britain was one of huge brick built factories and terrace after terrace of workers houses and, of course, the Empire and power. America, on the other hand, was a country of wooden textile mills, immigrant slums in the cities on the Atlantic coast, plantations and slaves in the South.

As for transport on land, you walked if you were poor. If you were rich you went by horse and carriage, or even steam locomotive, if tracks had been built the way that you intended to go. At sea the sailing ship ruled supreme. Tiny by today's standards, these little ships were tossed across the oceans by the whims of the elements. There were some smoky steam ships chugging around, but these were still somewhat of a novelty. The wheels of industry ground and squeaked round on animal fats and vegetable oils. In Europe they were powered by steam engines, while in America by water mills or just muscle and sweat. Home and factories were lit by disgusting, greasy, smoky, smelly candles and tallow lamps when the sun went down. No wonder work began at the crack of dawn so as to make the most of daylight hours.

This was the world into which the tanker was born. But oil itself was far from unknown. It had been used and written about for centuries. In many places around the world it used to, and for that matter still does, seep to the surface. It was these tell-tale signs, often on lakes or streams, which have led many an oil explorer to the right place. The quantities which made it to the surface by themselves were very small and so they were only ever used locally. In Burma, Rumania and Russia hand dug wells had been opened up much earlier than 1850 and in Britain, in 1847, James Young had established the

WORLD CRUDE OIL PRODUCTION: 1860 TO 1914

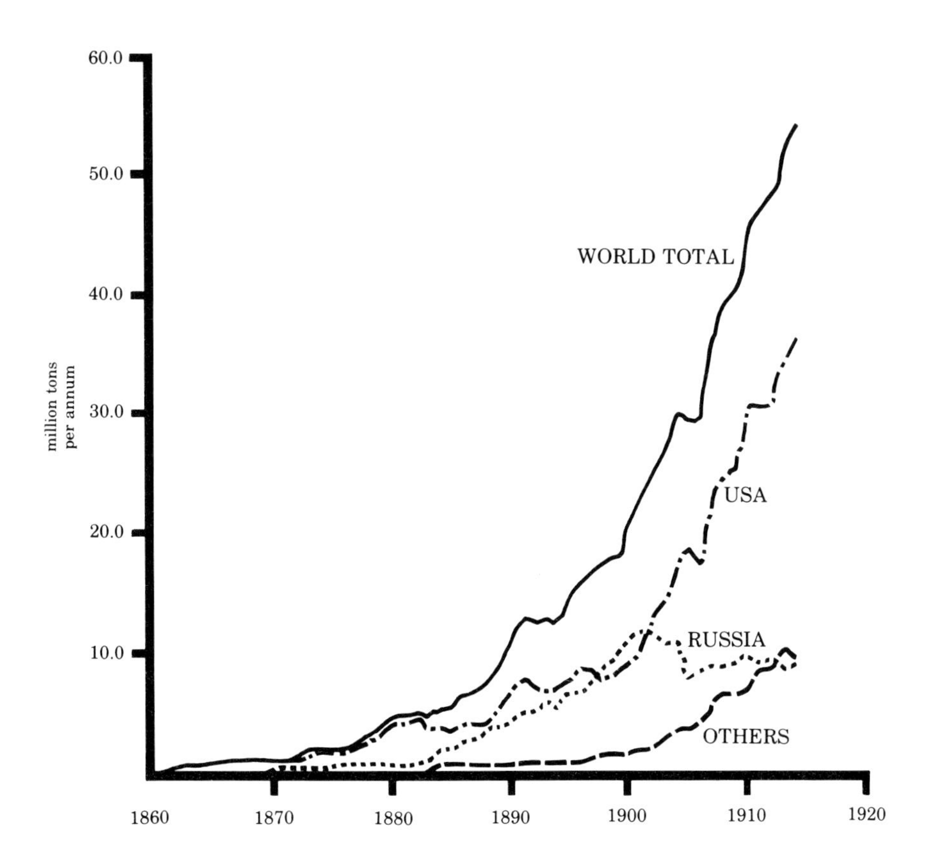

BREAKDOWN OF WORLD CRUDE OIL PRODUCTION

	USA	Other W. Hemi	Russia	Other Europe	Other E. Hemi	Total
1860	98%	—	—	2%	—	100%
1870	91%	4%	4%	1%	—	100%
1880	88%	1%	10%	1%	—	100%
1890	60%	1%	37%	2%	—	100%
1900	43%	1%	51%	3%	2%	100%
1910	64%	1%	21%	7%	7%	100%

(W. Hemi covers all lands in North, Central and South America plus the Caribbean)

first oil refining operation, using boghead coal and later Scottish shale oil — this even led to exports across the Atlantic of both oil products and the raw material which was processed under licence on the East Coast of America.

None of these operations was large enough to claim the privilege of being the start of the world oil industry which we know today. This began with a paper written by a Professor Silliman Junior of Yale College on petroleum from the natural springs of "Oil Creek" near Titusville in Pennsylvania in the North East of the USA. Again, oil from this area was nothing new. It had first been recorded as early as 1748 and produced from hand dug wells from 1840. This paper sparked off some interest in 1859 and a 'Colonel' Edwin Drake was sent to drill a test well. This was the first time anyone had made an active decision to drill for oil and, in the same year, at 69 feet 6 inches down, that decision brought, success.

News of Drake's find spread fast and soon everyone was in there drilling. All down Oil Creek, there were finds. Both north east and south west of Oil Creek there were finds. The American oil industry had been born. The "liquid gold diggers" who followed hot on Drake's heels opened up a huge oil belt nearly 200 miles long across Pennsylvania into West Virginia and Ohio, parallel to the East Coast, but some 300 long miles away from both the seaboard itself and the big city markets on it.

In these early days, the American oil industry was virtually a free-for-all. There was no sense of integration or co-operation either from the producers or from the multitude of tin-pot refiners who set up in and around Pittsburgh to process these new finds. By simply distilling off the volatile and dangerous light ends plus the dirty heavy ends, a magnificent new illuminating oil or "kerosine" could be produced. It gave off a steady, clear, bright light, was smokeless (well nearly smokeless) and did not smell. Oil was certainly wanted by the market. The only problem was how to get it there.

Roads were nearly non-existent where the oil had been found, and transportation further hampered by dense timber forests and mountains. Settlers had moved into this area only some 50 years earlier and then just onto the land that was worth farming. To begin with, the crude oil had to be moved over this inhospitable terrain from the wells to the refineries. Iron-hooped wooden barrels were used. They were pulled and pushed to the mouth of the Oil Creek by horse and cart and men. From there, they were loaded onto flat barges and floated down the Allegheny River, some 100 miles to the Pittsburgh area. At the junction of two rivers, Pittsburgh had become an important staging post for timber trades and even boasted of a large river boat building industry. Here the refiners set up. They distilled off the light ends that they wanted and then either burnt the 30–40% of unwanted crude or just threw it away (today none is unused and only 5–7% is burnt or lost in processing). The refined oil was again put into barrels and sent on the railway by railcar to the East Coast markets.

In 1862, the Atlantic and Great Western Railroad took the first step in easing the burden of getting oil out of the Creek. It extended its track right up to the oil producing region, displacing the river barges with flat railcars. Barrels were never an ideal solution for oil: they could all too easily leak or, if not handled carefully, split open. In 1865, therefore, special bulk railroad tankcars were built, using two 7-ton wooden vats mounted on flat railcars, to be superseded in 1871 by horizontal metal boiler cylinders.

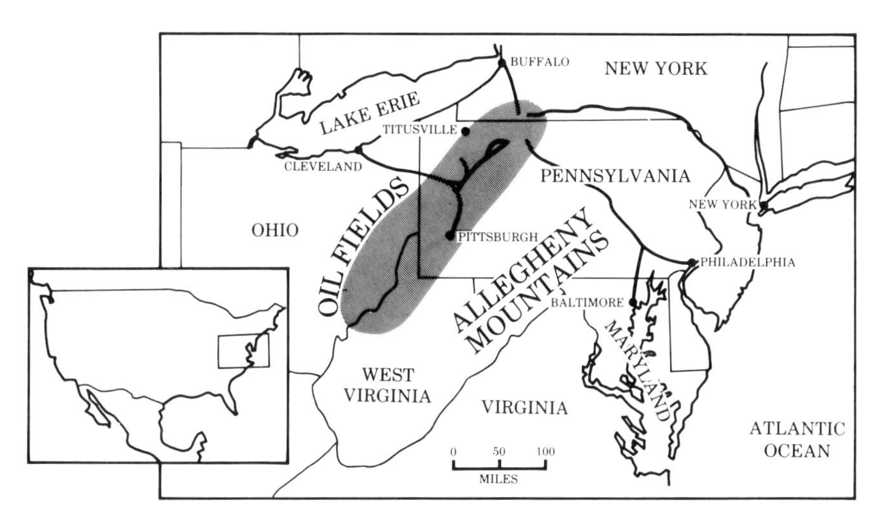

MAP OF NORTH-EAST U.S.A. OILFIELDS, PIPELINES AND EXPORT TERMINALS—C.A. 1890

Despite these improvements, the whole business of land transport to the East Coast remained tortuous and dangerous. Fire was a constant hazard and many a small entrepreneur found his business suddenly, and literally, going up in flames, creating a high risk, high profit and cutthroat market. It is, therefore, not surprising that the individual enterprises in this tenuous chain from the inland wells to the East Coast markets did not give much thought to rationalising their activities – they were far too busy keeping their own links in one piece. They certainly were not worried about the demands of faraway places like Europe.

But it was Europe who really wanted and, for that matter, could afford the new product. Petroleum was good not just for lamp oil, but also for lubricating oils, solvents and even tars. There was no way that at this stage it could compete with coal. It was just too expensive and in any case Europe's economy revolved around coal. There were many powerful interests invested in coal and it was to be a hard long fight before oil won over the big, primary fuel markets from coal. No, it was against the old vegetable and animal fats and oils that petroleum could immediately compete. The 1830s and '40s had been the heyday of whaling. Catches were now on the decline and demand for good quality substitutes was rising fast – to light the growing number of factories in the evenings and, at night, the new urban sprawls built up around the factories. Good quality lubricants were needed on both land and sea to keep the wheels of industry, and particularly of the steam engine running smoothly.

With the infant American oil industry completely involved in domestic survival, it was up to the European traders to come and get what they wanted. Ties with Europe and in particular Britain were very strong – it was less than a century since America had gained its freedom from being a British colony. Some three quarters of America's exports, mainly agricultural, went to Europe, while around two thirds of her imports, principally finished goods, came from Europe. Trade links across the Atlantic were good.

It was, in any case, Europe and Britain which had built up the sophisticated network of international traders, shippers, insurance brokers and financiers who were prepared to take the risks of crossing the high seas to get the goods Europe needed. America had its merchants on the East Coast, but their main concern was to get the goods to the Atlantic ports, not across the oceans. It was, therefore, the Americans who produced, refined and moved oil on land, but the Europeans who shipped it by sea . . . at least to begin with.

2 PARCELS UNDER SAIL

The challenge, then, from America to Europe was "come and get it" – and come they did, in the face of growing domestic American demand and highly volatile prices. Any new field coming on stream could temporarily swamp the market and send prices rocketing down, and any unexpected supply problems could just as easily force them up with little or no warning. In 1859, the average well head price of crude was $16 per barrel; in 1860 it had dropped to $9.59; by 1861 to $0.49. Then it steadily rose to a high of $8.06 per barrel in 1864 to fall back to $2.41 in 1867. For the rest of the century, average prices seasawed between lows of $0.50 and highs of $2.50 per barrel.

In the mid 19th century, the United States had a serious balance of trade deficit and needed exports. In 1864, therefore, only five years after the discovery of commercial Americal oil, 750,000 barrels or around 100,000 tons per year was being exported and nearly all to Europe, leaving only some 40–50% for the domestic US market. It was extremely convenient that the big US market was on the East Coast, such as the cities of New York and Philadelphia, built up by the emigrants from Europe in earlier centuries. The American industry, therefore, had the same destination for its oil movements, whether for the domestic market or for foreign exports, and it was here that the big US merchants with the links to Europe were based. Around 75% of these exports went through the port of New York and most of the remainder from Philadelphia.

As production grew and more and more became available for export, oil gradually became a recognisable seaborne trade in its own right for the first time in the history of shipping. It was, of course, no newcomer to the marine world. Just as oil had been known about for centuries, so had oil been shipped for centuries. The Greeks are recorded as carrying oil in 'fire ships' as long ago as 670 AD, but as a weapon, not as merchandise. In the 18th century, the Chinese had shipped small quantities – up to 50 tons – in bulk in junks which had originally been converted to carry water. At around the same time, the Persians were also carrying bulk oil in small craft on the Caspian Sea, the Russians on the Volga and the Burmese on the Irrawady.

The build-up of Atlantic trades was so rapid that it almost immediately outclassed these earlier experiments. However, it was never large by modern standards – totalling only 2.3 million tons per year by 1900, it was around enough to keep one modern 160,000-tonner fully employed and represented just 2% of world deepsea shipping. But it was an ocean trade, unlike the 18th century movements which were all on rivers or sheltered waters. It encountered the dangers of the open Atlantic and both the volumes and distances it was transported over were quite unprecedented.

When movements started in the 1860s, very few shippers attempted to use anything other than the tried and tested methods. Virtually all goods at that time were shipped in small, conveniently sized parcels as general cargo. The world did not want big deliveries – mass markets had yet to be created. Atlantic cargo shipping, in the mid-19th century, was composed of small sailing craft. Although the steamship had been in regular use on the Atlantic since 1838, even by 1860 these vessels of 1,000 to 2,000 tons* were still very expensive and could only be kept in service through heavy government subsidies, principally for regular mail shipments. Apart from mail, the only other cargo which could afford to be carried on these steam packets were passengers. Low value commodities, which included humble oil, had to be content with the far cheaper, traditional sailing ship.

There was a wide range of choice between the many available types and sizes of sailing ships. There was a huge number of very small 100 to 200 ton vessels braving the waters of the Atlantic, often owned by the master, which tramped around looking for cargo. These were mainly two-masted brigs or two- to three-masted schooners, some 100 feet in length. The first ever full cargo of oil to cross the Atlantic went in just such a ship: the 224 ton brig (c. 350 DWT), *Elizabeth Watts*, owned by Mr. E. A. Sanders. She sailed from Philadelphia to London in late 1861, carrying 1,329 barrels at a rate of 8 shillings a barrel, some £3 a ton. Even before this voyage – undertaken by the merchants Peter Wright & Sons – there had been a number of part cargoes of only 25 to 50 barrels shipped by this company. With the ever present problem of leaking

*"Tons" generally meant Gross Registered Tons (GRT) and approximately equalled ⅔ of Deadweight (DWT)

barrels, they had been stowed well forward, to avoid contaminating other cargo.

At the other end of the scale, sailing ships ranged up to 1,000 to 3,000 tons and these larger vessels fell into two broad categories. There were the lumbering old-style vessels, European in origin and built for trading long distances, such as to the Far East. Many were elderly British ships, built to serve her far-flung colonies – typical products of the world-leading, but stagnant shipbuilding and owning industries which she had built up on the back of her monopolistic colonial trades. In complete contrast were the clippers, the modern class of sailing ship. Developed by the Americans during the 1840s, the clipper to begin with was not so much a unique design of ship, but rather a fast version of any traditional vessel type which could 'clip' time off the old voyage times. To gain this extra speed, the hull design was modified to make it longer and narrower than the old European classes.

Once this new design had proved its worth, any ship built and rigged for speed tended to be called a clipper. The riggings generally favoured for these large modern ships were five- to six-masted schooner rigging for up to 3,000 tons and five-masted barque rigging for the very big ships of up to 6,000 tons. They were incredibly successful, principally through their much higher speeds, and soon dominated the long haul routes with good trade winds – to the Far East or around Cape Horn to the West Coast of America. The clipper came along just at the time when Britain and the rest of Europe were discarding the old restrictive maritime trade laws and opening up their cargoes for any ship owner to carry.

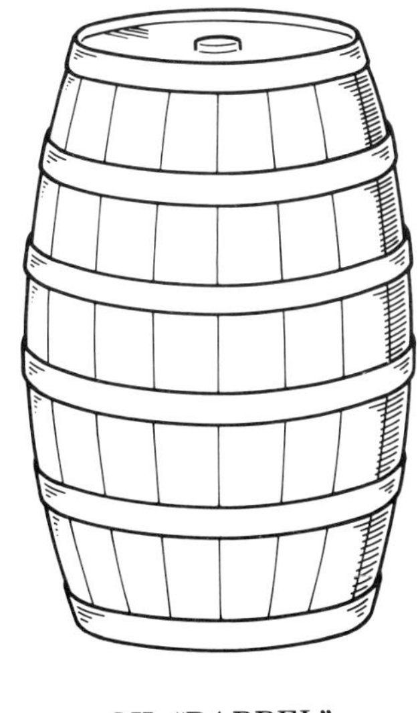

OIL "BARREL"

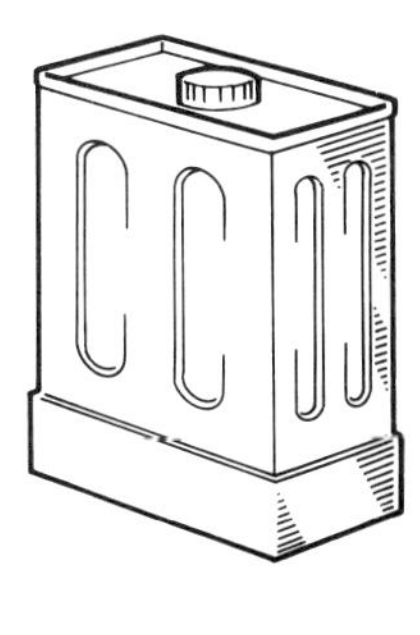

OIL "TIN"

The cheap soft woods of the American East Coast could compete more than favourably with the dwindling and, thus, expensive hard woods of Southern England. With the growing demand for fast, cheap, open market tonnage, the American shipyards on the East Coast went through a tremendous boom in wooden ship construction. Although America could not supply all the sophisticated gear, tackle, anchors and sailcloth for these ships, Europe could. European merchants, therefore, sent ship loads of these and other finished goods across the Atlantic for sale in America. On the proceeds, a new ship was often built to order and when fitted out, loaded with excellent American white pine timbers for her maiden voyage back to her European owners.

In its early years, it tended to be the smaller, older types of sailing ship which were used for oil – they could take a full ship load in this limited volume trade. While the great wealthy European and, particularly, British shipyards were investing money and expertise in developing the steamship, there remained dozens of smaller yards which could not afford the same engineering skills or new equipment, or which, simply through limited water depths, could only build the sailing ship. Many of the larger yards went in for clippers in response to American competition, while all-purpose traders, cheap and small enough to call at any port, were still turned out in their hundreds.

Whatever vessel was used for oil, some form of container to carry the oil had to be used. Just like any other cargo of the time, it had to be "parcelled up" for the voyage. Barrels* were the obvious answer. They were used for long enough on both land and sea to become a standard measure in the oil industry (1 barrel = 42 US gallons – in the 1860s for every 40 gallons sold, US producers gave an allowance of 2 gallons to the refiners). They were certainly a more practical solution than the glass jars used in the early Burmese oil industry! The standard barrel was 33 inches long and 25 inches in diameter. It was made from white oak, glued, reinforced with six or eight metal hoops, painted blue with a white bottom, and fitted with a good two-inch bung.

Only the very best, first class barrels, could be used for the more volatile clean products, 2nd class were permitted for crude oil and 3rd class only for the residuum. Despite this basic safety classification, no barrel, however well made, proved eminently suitable for the transport of a dangerous liquid like petroleum. Leakage was possibly anything from 5% to 12% of the contents. Although on land this was just another messy problem, in the confined cargo hold of a ship in mid-ocean, the vapours given off could turn the ship into a "floating bomb". There was, therefore, a constant danger of explosion and fire: so much so, that the crew of the *Elizabeth Watts* viewed her historic cargo with intense fear and, rather than risk being burnt alive in their bunks, deserted. The master, a Captain Charles Bryant, had to resort to scraping up a scratch crew from the local bars of Philadelphia – an ignominious beginning indeed for

*Barrels had been used at sea for centuries and even the shipping term "tonnage" comes from the French for barrel "tonneaux" – in the 13th century wooden barrels had been used to ship wine to Britain and had become the standard measure of a ship's carrying capacity.

EARLY TANK SAILERS

"Newchwang Junk", early 18th century, some 45 ft. in length and carried some 50 tons of oil. (Source: Tanker Technique 1936)

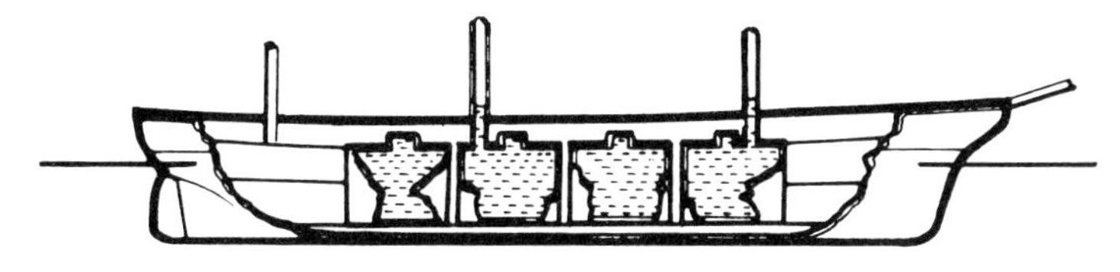

1863. The "Atlantic", built of iron in 1863, was designed for transatlantic trade. She had four tanks, and two of her masts served as expansion trunks. She was wrecked after a life of only six years. Some 160 ft. in length. (Source: "The Worlds Tankers", Laurence Dunn, 1956)

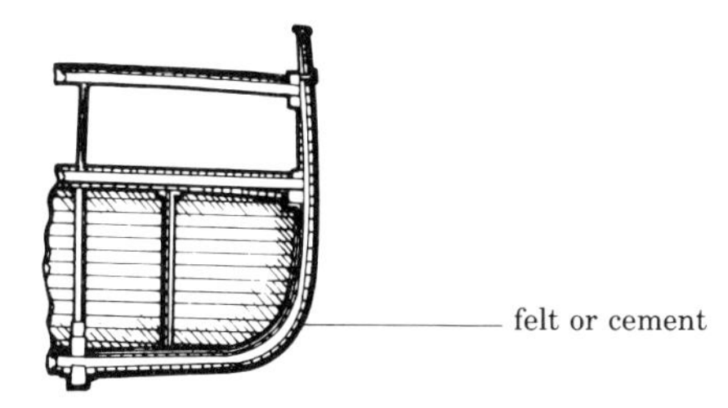

1878. Half section of a typical wooden ship designed to carry oil in bulk, and built about 1878. Surge of the liquid cargo was reduced by the fitting of fore and aft washboards approximately midway between the centreline bulkhead and the sides of the hull, which were lined with either cement or felt. "Fanny" 1153GRT had cement lining whilst "Lindesures" had felt.

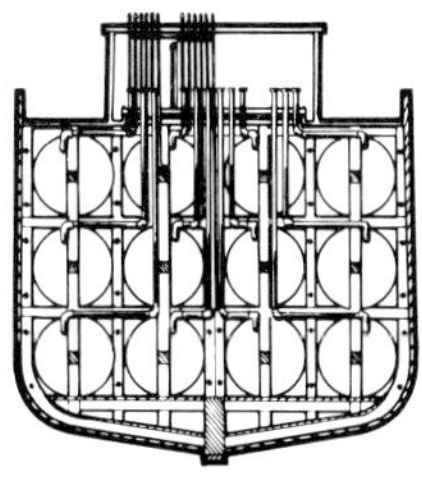

The American wooden barque tank-sailer "Crusader" with 3 tiers of horizontal cylindrical tanks, 47 in total. Built around 1885.

what was eventually to become the world's most important seaborne trade.

Leakage and fire were not the only problems of the barrel. They stowed badly wasting a lot of space between them – a 2,000 ton capacity ship could only load 1,250 tons of barrelled goods. They also could never be completely filled, in case the oil became warmer, expanded and burst the barrel's seams. They also weighed too much, accounting for one sixth of their filled weight, so reducing the paying cargo on board a 2,000 tonner to just over 1,000 tons. They were also troublesome when empty: as the main trades were only one way, eastbound across the Atlantic, shippers either had to sell empties at 3s 6d compared with a cost in America of 5s, and so incur a loss, or ship them back and pay the combined costs of backhaul freight, import duty into the USA and repairs to any damaged barrels.

Barrels were clearly not the answer. So in 1865, a refiner, Charles Pratt, hired a German inventor, Herman Miller, to come up with a better solution. His idea was the rectangular tin canister capable of carrying 5 US gallons. Generally carried in pairs (sometimes fours) in wooden "cases" of 20¾ inches by 15 inches by 10½ inches, these stowed much better than barrels and weighed less. Even more important, these tins could be sealed with solder, fitted with screw caps and if finished properly were virtually leakproof, even in tropical climates.

Tins also had important marketing advantages over barrels. The 10-gallon "double pack", at around a quarter of a barrel, was a much more convenient sized parcel for the final customer and even looked more attractive – provided the tins did not go rusty before being sold. They even had their uses for the buyers when empty, particularly in the less developed parts of the world where consumers became used to a regular supply of free tins for roofing or cooking pots. Consequently he put up considerable resistance when the oil industry later developed other forms of packaging. However, the shippers were not in the free gifts business. The big disadvantage of tins was that they were astronomically expensive, accounting for over 50% of the final retail cost of the oil, partly because the metal itself was costly, partly because the tins had to be given away, but mainly because the tin had to be shipped from Wales to the tinning factories in Europe and America. Cases did not overcome the expensive manhandling – it could still take up to a week to load or unload one of the small Atlantic sailing ships.

As the volumes of oil from the States built up, so did the shipping problems. The traditional general cargo tramp sailers could only handle limited volumes and the consumer could not afford to pay them high freight charges. This method of deepsea shipping could not be the ultimate solution for oil if volumes continued to grow.

3 EXPERIMENTS IN BULK SHIPPING

Parcel shipment, although the obvious and, indeed, the only choice of transportation in the early days – both on land and at sea – was clearly not the most desirable in the longer term. The high costs made less and less sense and inevitably enterprising shippers looked for alternative and more efficient means of containment.

The most logical solution was to replace the small, heavy and space-consuming barrels and even tins with much larger containers. Then, rather than having to manhandle each and every small container into and out of the ship, the oil could be directly pumped into and out of the container itself. Compared with the five to six days it took to load or discharge package oil cargoes, these bulk shipments should only take five or six hours. Early experiments along these lines were many and varied: the most simplistic were attempts in the late 1870s to convert ordinary wooden sailing ships to "floating tanks" by just pouring oil into the hull. Since the weather on the Atlantic was often foul and dangerous, it was out of the question just to fill up an unprotected wooden hull with oil. A group of French merchants, therefore, tried lining the wooden cargo space of three Norwegian vessels with felt: the 375 GRT (600 DWT) *Lindesnoes*, *Nordkyn*, and *Jan Mayn*, and one 1,153 GRT (2,000 DWT) vessel with cement: the *Fanny*. The *Nordkyn* went aground in Delaware River in 1879, the *Fanny* left Philadelphia in 1880 with her first cargo of crude oil for Europe never to be heard of again and the *Jan Mayn* disappeared after a few voyages. The experiment was definitely not a success, but it was this first attempt to create a bulk oil carrier for the deep sea by using the hull itself as the container.

The preferred method of creating a bulk container for Atlantic oil was not to use wood but metal. Iron ships had first appeared in the 1820s, mainly as products of British ship yards, which with the back up of the advanced British metal industry recognised the advantages of the metal hull and had the expertise to exploit it. The first experiments had been with compound iron ribbed and wooden planked hulls, a useful compromise, which remained popular for many years. The first iron ribbed and plated vessel was built as early as 1836, but it was ahead of its time and the all metal hull did not receive general acceptance for the high seas until the 1880s.

This climate of opinion meant that the iron hull, despite its obvious safety advantages over the wooden hull, was not considered seriously for bulk oil transport during the 1860s and '70s: it was feared that oil would weaken the riveting and hence the hull, and that the movement of bulk oil in high seas could cause fatal stresses and possible breakup of the entire ship. There is good reason to believe that these fears were well grounded, since early riveting techniques were a primitive affair.

The compromise between small parcels and a large "floating tank" came in the form of a double containment system with a number of separate metal tanks being installed within the existing hull design. The advantage of this principle was that the main hull was protected from stresses, and either wooden or metal ships proved suitable carriers. Any leakages from an internal tank would collect in the hull and losses to the sea could be minimised.

As early as 1863, only two years after the *Elizabeth Watts* consignment, the first of these two-containment "tank ships" came into service, and viable deepsea bulk oil carriers were created. In that year the iron hulled sailing ship *Ramsey* was built for a Mr. Gibson of the Isle of Man: she was a tank sailer capable of carrying 1,400 tons of oil in her specially designed iron tanks, as well as in barrels in her 'tween deck.

In the same year a smaller iron ship, the *Atlantic*, of 416 tons, was built on the Tyne in Britain. She too had special iron tanks, eight in all, fitted inside her hull, as did her sistership the *Great Western*. Both carried around 700 tons of oil and were owned by the Petroleum Trading Company. This company was established by the Newcastle firm of Rogerson & Sons, one of the first English merchant houses to invest in the new Atlantic oil trade. Following the completion of the Atlantic and Great Western Railway in the USA in 1862, Rogerson's was immediately set up and entered into a supply agreement with the new railway to New York. They then announced that they were "the largest importer in the trade".

Unfortunately the *Atlantic* was wrecked after only six years. In the year she went down, 1869, another sailing ship, the *Charles*, was converted to carry 794 tons of oil in 59 square iron tanks. As with most ships of this time, she had two

OCEAN-GOING TANK STEAMERS

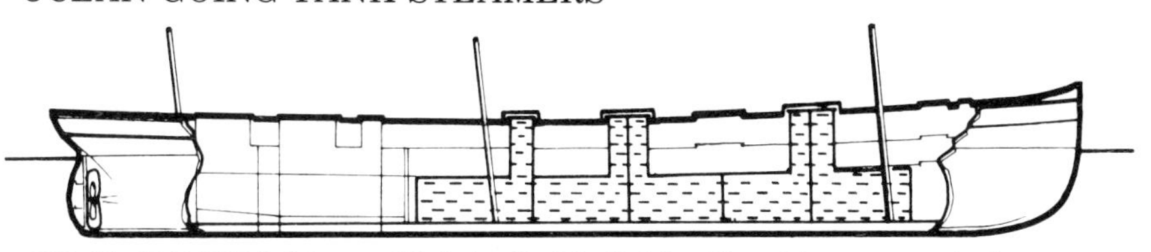

1872. The 2748 GRT Belgian s.s. "Vaderland" of the Red Star Line of Antwerp was the first steamer designed to carry petroleum in bulk; there are, however, no records of her being used for this. Built at Jarrow in 1872, she measured 320 ft. in length. Her engines were placed aft, and her passenger accommodation flanked the expansion trunks.

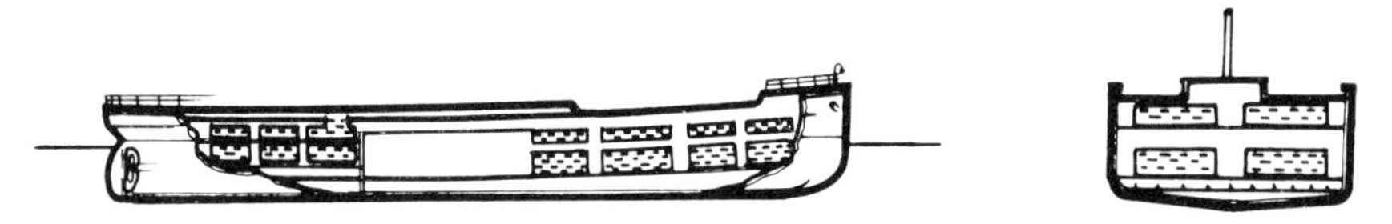

1880. The "Fergusons" was converted in 1885 to a tank steamer with tanks installed in her 'tweendecks by Messrs Craggs & Sons of Middlesbrough, UK. She carried some 1,500/2,000 tons of oil from Batum to North Europe via the Black Sea and the Mediterranean and was the first tank ship to sail from Batum to the UK.

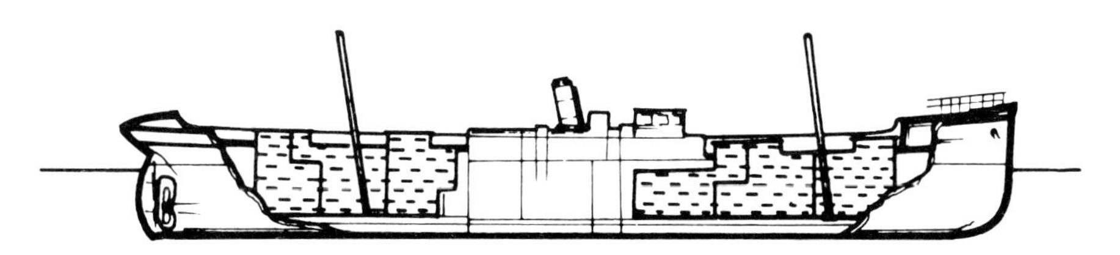

1886. The s.s. "Chigwell", a dry cargo ship, which in 1886 was converted to carry oil in bulk. She measured 250 ft. in length by 34.5 ft. beam, and had a DW capacity of 2,150 tons. A very successful ship, she lasted well into this century, finishing up as an oil barge in Far Eastern waters.

decks, the lower being the main deck and the space between this and the upper was the 'tween deck space. These tanks were fitted in two rows in both her main hold and her 'tween deck. She could be loaded in only six hours. However, her tanks were not good and leaked, but that mattered little since her master was a resourceful man and simply topped them up with sea water. The *Charles* had an even shorter life, being destroyed by fire after only three years of trading on the Atlantic.

The natural hazard of fire incurred by all these ships trading in oil was to some degree exacerbated by the two-containment design. The dead spaces between and under the tanks could never be cleaned or repaired properly; minor leakages collected in them and the explosive vapours were therefore trapped, ready for the first spark to set them alight.

This did not prevent designers from extending the tank ship design to carry passengers as well as cargo. In 1872, the 2,748 GRT (4,000 DWT) steamship *Vaderland* was built in Britain by Messrs Palmer & Co for a Philadelphia company with the capability of carrying both bulk oil and passengers for the first voyage from the USA to Antwerp. She was the first 'tank steamer' but in practice neither she nor her sisterships, the *Nederland* (1873) and the *Switzerland* (1874) carried oil until the 1880s at the earliest. The Belgian authorities refused to allow the necessary land tankage to be built and the US put a ban on carrying oil in passenger ships: it is hardly likely in any case that passengers would have elected to cross the Atlantic with the inevitable fumes from leakages and spills.

The trading opportunities for these early tank sailers and steamers were very restricted. By 1870, Atlantic exports to Europe were only around 0.3 million tons per year and by 1880 still no more than 0.8m tons per year. This slow rate of growth in no way reflected on the enthusiasm of the European importers, but only the limited production in the States and so the inability of the American industry to get any greater volumes to the Atlantic Coast.

This small oil trade was, in any case, destined for over 40 different European ports. Since it was rare for an individual importer to be involved in any great number of ports, the seaborne oil flows under the control of any one shipper tended to be limited – far too limited for all but the largest importers operating in the main European ports to consider using a large, inflexible specialist ship which might carry some 5 or 10,000 tons of oil per year and which was only useful for the one-way flow of oil across the Atlantic. Tramp sailers, by contrast, could carry any cargo either way. There was also a significant lack of bulk tankage on the seaboard to feed or receive these large vessels; although some small tank farms were built, the export trade was too small to justify investment in facilities of a really practical size. With all these problems, the small independent trader or merchant simply could not risk his own limited capital in such new ventures in the 1860s and '70s, especially when there were so many small sailing craft readily available to ship barrels.

So, despite the obvious technical and economic advantages of the tank sailer, even by 1885 there were only 10 of these newfangled vessels running the Atlantic, some iron-hulled and some wooden-hulled with internal rectangular or cylindrical iron tanks. Although the carrying capacity of these ships was several times greater than that of the small sailing ship carrying barrels or tins, in the mid-1880s around 90% of the oil crossing the Atlantic was still being moved in parcel not bulk shipments.

4 THE BAKU REVOLUTION

Once oil had been found in commercial quantities in America, European appetite for the new illuminator and lubricant was whetted. Throughout the rest of the century a widespread search went on for oilfields closer to home. Although oil was discovered and produced in many parts of Europe – Galicia, Italy and Germany, as well as expansion of the old Rumanian fields – yields were limited and it was only in Russia that Europe found a really important oil producing region. Here, the world's second big oil industry grew up, with a massive output which even surpassed American production for the four years 1898–1901.

Russian oil was first produced in large quantities in the south of the country around the inland Caspian Sea, near Balakhani, a few miles north west of the seaside town of Baku. This region had had a long history of production; Marco Polo reported seeing oil exploitation here in the 13th century. Limited production from hand-dug wells continued up to the 19th century, the oil being carried in sheepskin bags from the wells. However, it was not until 1871 that oil was produced in commercial quantities from a drilled well and 1872 that the Russian Government stopped its monopoly and opened up the land for anyone to lease for exploration. Thirteen years behind the American industry, Russia started its oil rush.

The state of the Russian oil industry in the 1870s and early 1880s, and particularly its distribution systems, differed greatly from its American

MAP OF SOUTH-WEST RUSSIAN OILFIELDS, PIPELINES, RAILWAYS AND EXPORT TERMINALS—*c.* 1900

counterparts. The American entrepreneurs could afford to concentrate purely on land distribution to their East Coast markets, in the knowledge that European importers would arrange sea transport if they wanted the oil enough – which in fact they did. Russian industry did not have it this easy. The producing area near Baku was over 1,000 miles from its prime market in the Russian Empire – Moscow and the other important Russian cities – and even further away from the potentially lucrative demand of North West Europe. The railway from Moscow came halfway to the oil fields, to Tsaritsyn (nowadays Stalingrad) on the Volga. But between the railway terminal and the Baku lay some 200 miles of the Volga where only shallow draft barges could be used and over 500 miles of land-locked Caspian Sea from Astrakhan.

Unlike the American producers, the Russians were forced from the start to look at sea transportation from the Baku to the mouth of the Volga as an essential link in the distribution chain – not only to the Russian cities but onwards to North West Europe. The alternative route west overland to the

Black Sea and then via the Mediterranean to the North Sea was unthinkable at that time; there was no railroad and over 400 miles of mountainous terrain to be covered.

The Caspian-Volga route for oil was not a new one and oil was not a new commodity as it was in America: regulations for bulk shipments of oil on the Volga had been introduced by the Russian authorities as early as 1725. The movement to regular bulk shipping on the Caspian, therefore, came naturally to the developing Russian oil industry. By 1871, three profiteering Astrakahn merchants, Rogosin, Artemjeff and Schipott, had begun to move crude and residual oils in vessel hulls rather than in barrels. Although this was not the first time oil had been carried this way on the Caspian, this partnership started a general craze for this highly dangerous method of sea carriage. They loaded the decks of their wooden sailing ships and barges with barrels and iron tanks filled with oil, then loaded the hulls with oil up to the waterline, trusting that the external pressure of the water would stop the oil leaking out of the hulls.

Soon there were large numbers of these primitive tankers on both the Caspian and the Volga: a fashion encouraged by the dramatic fall in oil prices created when the Russian government stopped monopolising production in 1872, forcing the industry to reduce transportation costs and so accept bulk shipping on the Caspian Sea as the norm. However, the shippers' trust in external water pressure proved sadly misplaced. Oil soon penetrated the wooden hulls, and there were frequently disastrous fires. A case worth recalling is that of a seaman, who lowered a lighted candle by a string into an oil barge to see how much oil was on board. The candle burnt the string, which fell into the oil and the whole barge exploded.

It is highly unlikely that these risky ventures into bulk oil shipping would of themselves have led to the sophisticated sea transport systems which Russia was to enjoy in the second half of the 1870s. Fortunately for the Russian oil industry, it experienced a degree of rationalisation and control unknown in the early American industry, at a very early stage in its development. The lead was given by a single organisation owned by two Swedish brothers, the Nobels.

They acquired their first productive well in 1874; in 1875 they opened a refinery at Baku (its refining suburb was to earn itself the name of Blacktown), and in 1877 ran a crude oil pipeline over the seven miles from the wells to the refinery, replacing the painfully slow horse-and-cart method which had been used to start with. From this firm base, the Nobels rapidly established a monopoly over shipping on the Caspian, and when limited supplies of wood for barrels forced them to consider alternative transport means, they had the strength to invest in completely new and revolutionary types of bulk oil carriers – unlike the Atlantic traders who had to develop with great caution. The Nobels did not bother with the antics of the small merchants with their primitive wooden tankers. They learned from the experiments of the European shippers, and immediately went to the true tank sailer used and tested on the Atlantic, with metal cylinders installed inside the hulls of sailing ships.

However, their systematic and coordinated approach soon allowed them to overhaul the Europeans technically.

In 1878, the *Zoraster* was delivered: the world's first tank steamer, if we discount the *Vaderland* and her sisterships which, after all, were built for dual purpose use and had not at this date carried oil at all. Since only wooden ships could be built on the Caspian, the Nobels turned to their homeland, Sweden, and to Sven Almqvist of the Motala Shipyards at Norrköping and Lindholmen for their craft. The *Zoraster* was designed to carry around 250 tons of kerosine in 21 vertical cylindrical tanks within her iron hull: this design, known as a "cistern steamer" was not too different from the Nobels' earlier tank sailers. Later, however, these tanks were taken out so that oil could be carried directly next to her iron hull. In order to stop oil leaking from the cargo tanks into the engine room, a partition was filled with water which was continuously renewed and any oil leakages ran off the top.

The *Zoraster* was also revolutionary in that she burnt fuel oil, not coal or wood – a development not seen on the Atlantic until the 20th Century. Russian crude was much heavier than American. The black residue amounted to 60 to 70% compared with only 20% in American crude. To begin with, as in America, this residue was thrown away with the too volatile light end. The Russians realised that it would burn very well then, so "mazout" or fuel oil became a ready substitute for coal around the Caspian. The Russian state railway as well as steamships on the Caspian soon began to use it and it became equally as important a product as kerosine as early as the 1880s, although unlike kerosine it was not exported for many years.

In 1879, the *Nordenskiöld* and the *Buddha* were delivered by the Nobels. Not only did these vessels have cisterns installed but, amidships, they had three long tanks formed by four longitudinal bulkheads inside the hull, leaving wing spaces.

These tanks stood on a platform deck, the space underneath was also filled with oil, directly against the hull plating. Although not a true tanker, as defined by a classification society, these two vessels showed a major step towards using the hull itself as the final container of oil. The next vessel for the Nobels went even further. The *Moses*, built at Lindholmen in 1880/1 had two cisterns and the machinery aft. Amidships, there were four oil tanks formed by both sides of the hull and the bottom.

The fledgling tanker had arrived. By 1882, the Nobels had 12 oil-burning steam bulk oil carriers on the Caspian, some with oil being contained by the hull itself, some with part of the cargo space filled by separate cylindrical metal tanks, and some with dry cargo capacity aft of the engine space (which was amidships, as with nearly all steam ships at that time). As well as these tankers and tankships, they also built up a fleet of tank barges for the Volga. All this was well in advance of developments on the Atlantic, where up to the mid-1880s European shippers were still predominantly transporting American oil across the Atlantic in parcel shipments under sail, and where iron-hulled,

CASPIAN SEA TANK STEAMERS

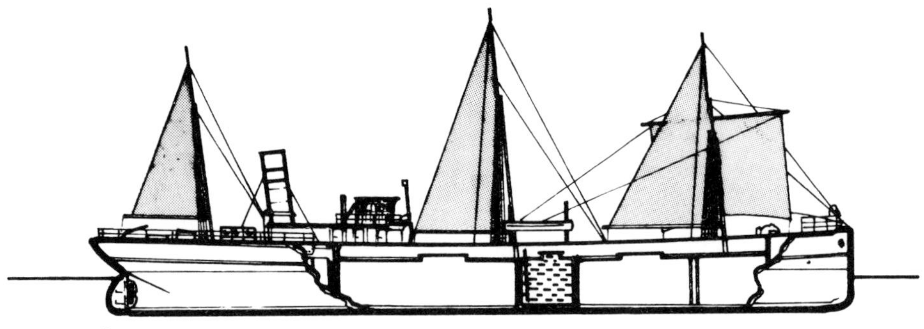

"Massis"

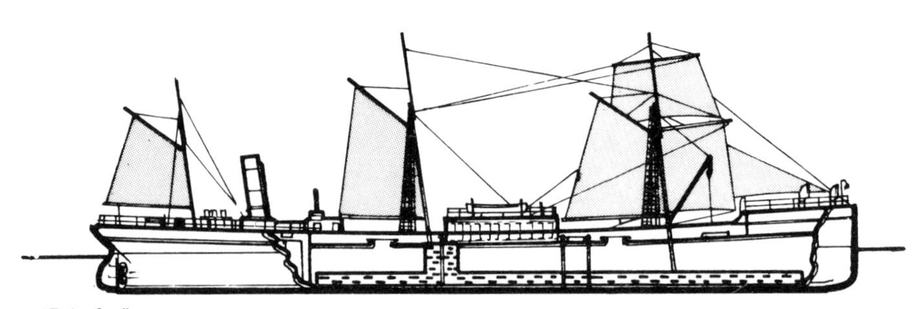

"Poisedon"

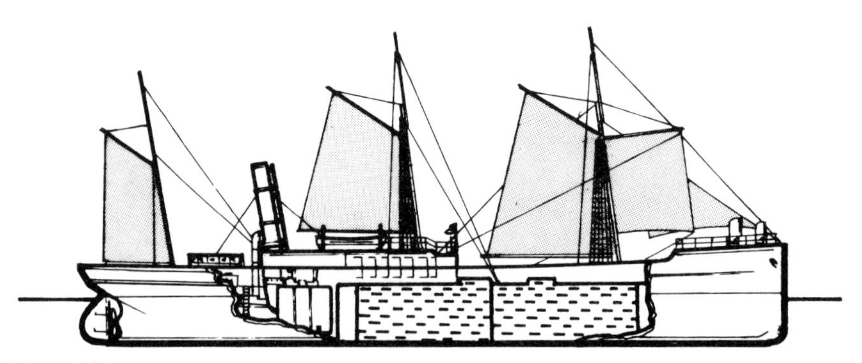

"Armeniak"

Three vessels built in 1883 for Caspian service by Armstrong, Whitworth (UK). The "Massis" could carry some 70 tons and the "Poisedon" 300 tons. Both these vessels also carried case oil whilst the "Armeniak" was built as a tanker.

steam-driven tankers did not appear until the late 1880s, nearly 10 years after the Caspian developments.

It must be remembered, of course, that there were considerable differences between the inland Caspian Sea conditions and those on the Atlantic. The Caspian could have very severe storms, but the seas were never as bad as the Atlantic in the winter. On the Caspian, land was never more than 80 miles away. Added to this, the transatlantic crossing was over seven times as long as the trip from Baku to the Volga. Even so, the Nobels must take the credit for helping to evolve the "modern" deepsea tanker, as must the Motala yards, as well as exercising a major influence in the future development of tanker design.

A section of the early Balakhany oil field in the Baku.

5 ATLANTIC ENTERPRISE

It was 10 years or more before the kind of integrated control exercised by the Nobels in Russia from the early 1870s was matched in America. The rationalisation of the oil transportation industry, on land at least, originated in 1875, when the Pennsylvanian Transportation Company was given permission to construct a pipeline from the oil producing region to the East Coast: an ambitious undertaking in view of the totally new technology involved, the significant distance of some 300 miles to cover, and, notably the Allegheny Mountains to bypass.

When it was completed in the late 1870s, the pipeline's impact was immediate and dramatic. First, of course, it brought a massively increased flow of oil to the East Coast, compared with the old rail route. No less important, it reduced land transportation costs so much that, for the first time in the history of the oil industry, it became economic to refine at the consuming end, since the lowered costs swallowed up the significant diseconomies of transporting the 30–40% unwanted light and heavy ends of the barrel – traditionally flared off, run to waste or burned in the refinery. This change in pattern from refining at the production end was reinforced by the very natural fear that piping oil products – in other words, kerosine – down 300 miles of line, over harsh terrain, would be far too hazardous to attempt.

New, large refineries sprang up and old whale oil plants were converted at New York, Philadelphia and Baltimore to cope with the new demand for coastal processing and with them came large tank farms to store the increasing volume of products. This removed the stumbling block to bulk carrier exports presented by the small old specialist tank farms, which had restricted the size of cargo and hence the viable size of a bulk oil vessel. The new large tankage facilities associated with the coastal refineries overcame these problems; they were easily financed as part of overall refinery projects, were available for both domestic and export needs, and greatly increased export flexibility. Along with the refineries came not only tankage but pumps and also technical expertise, needed for bulk handling. Suddenly the cost to an individual trader of developing from parcel shipments to specialised bulk oil vessels dropped substantially.

The new facilities were not enough in themselves to stimulate a massive investment in special purpose oil vessels. The European importing trader still needed guaranteed oil flows and security of supply before investing with confidence. He needed the kind of strongly controlled and integrated industry the Nobels had given Russia 10 years earlier, and he got what he needed with the American answer to the Nobels, Standard Oil.

Incorporated in 1870 with John D. Rockefeller as President, Standard Oil was by far the most important oil group to emerge from America until the early 20th century. It was mainly as a result of vertical integration. Rockefeller had been disgusted by the wastefulness of the multitude of early small American refiners and in the 1860s had decided to rationalise them. He soon had two refineries, a barrel-making plant and railtank cars. Although Rockefeller never entered oil exploration and production in a large way, over the next 20 years he built up his control of the American oil industry from production onwards, by amalgamating or buying his way into distribution networks, refineries and marketing. By the early 1880s, Standard Oil controlled 30% of US crude oil production, over 75% of refining capacity, more than 90% of pipelines, had a major stake in US railtank cars, and was in a unique position to influence both domestic and export markets.

Although there was a marked slowdown in export growth rate as Rockefeller concentrated on building up the lucrative home market, it was very much in Standard Oil's interests to keep domestic suppiles within reasonable limits and to maintain prices. This policy left substantial surpluses which could profitably be sold overseas; the "Standard", as the company became known, therefore began to forge international links with Western European importers in order to exercise as much control over its export profits as it did in the home markets. It did this by buying into European companies or even crushing an unwilling partner with price wars if necessary. This strategy of control through involvement succeeded and soon the Standard earned the better (?) title of the "Octopus". It had gained effective control over the total international supply of all American oil. For those European importers who had not been brought into the Standard empire, there was a new atmosphere of security in the supply networks – as long as they did not try to fight it!

By 1889, US exports had risen under the influence of the Standard to 14,700,000 barrels, or nearly 2 million tons, per year (compared with 0.8m in 1880, 0.3m in 1870 and 0.1m in 1864). This continued to represent about 40–50% of total American product output, just over half remaining for the home market. These exports were still principally for Europe, and still around 80% kerosine, 5% other refined products and 15% crude oil. The principal reason for the crude exports was to feed France where, up to 1903, a very heavy import tariff of 15–18 cents per barrel was placed on refined products compared with only 1¼ cents per barrel on crude oil, the purpose being to stimulate domestic refining. Although the policy succeeded in virtually prohibiting refined product imports, it also resulted in ensuring the supply of the worst quality crude.

With 1½ million tons of oil in regular and guaranteed transit across the Atlantic by 1885, the demand for specialist ships which could carry oil in bulk rather than in barrels grew rapidly. Parcel shipments, which even in 1885 still accounted for 90% of all deepsea oil movements, were becoming absurdly expensive as export volumes multiplied, and to make things worse barrels were now in short supply on the East Coast.

Forced by circumstances and encouraged by the greatly improved trading opportunities and facilities for bulk vessels, shippers began to take tank sailers much more seriously. Conversion of old sailing ships was a relatively cheap process and large numbers of these ships were now fitted out with virtually every conceivable size and shape of tank. There were square tanks and cylindrical tanks, vertical and horizontal. Old tramps were converted resulting in rows of tanks on each deck. Some of these vessels maintained some general cargo space as well as bulk oil capacity and to stop contamination from oil leakages double transverse bulkheads or "cofferdams" had to be installed between the oil and the other cargo space.

Most of the old wooden hulled vessels could carry between 2,000 and 3,000 tons of oil, but the tank sailer fleet was also enlarged by newer, bigger metal-hulled sailing ships built in considerable numbers in the late 19th century (and even up to the First World War). Because metal hulls were stronger than wood, were easier to handle and a better insurance risk (from fire and grounding angles), they were much more suitable for large ships – anything up to 10,000 DWT. An iron ship also had a higher potential speed and more carrying capacity than a wooden vessel of the same size, since its hull weighed only 70% as much. The introduction of steel in 1886 reduced hull weight by a further 20–30% and by 1890 had virtually completely superseded iron for newbuildings.

Converted tank sailers, whether metal or wooden with old or new hulls, provided cheap and plentiful tonnage for the increasing oil flows to Europe, especially at a time when many sailing ships were being made redundant by the growth of steam on the important world routes they had previously dominated. Many of these ships were of the modern clipper class. They could

THE LAST OF THE DEEPSEA TANK SAILERS

The "Brilliant", built for the Anglo-American Oil Co. Ltd. in 1901 by Russell & Co., Port Glasgow. She had a steel hull, measured 352.5 ft. × 49.1 ft. and was originally used as a case oil carrier, although she and her sister "Daylight" were later converted to carry oil in bulk. Each had a single oil-cargo pump of 100 tons capacity.

The "Thomas W. Lawson", 5,218 tons gross. The world's only seven-masted schooner, she was built by the Fore River S.B. Co., Quincy, Mass., in 1902. After early use on the U.S. coast carrying coal, she was converted into a bulk oil carrier. She was wrecked on the Scilly Islands in December, 1907. (Source: "The World's Tankers", Laurence Dunn, 1956)

not, however, compete with British metal-hulled steamships, and the second half of the 19th century saw the slow death of sail in all major trades. In 1860, 20% of the world's merchant fleet was steam powered, by 1880 40%, and by 1900, 90%. Oil was in fact one of the last refuges of the deepsea sailing ship, giving it a new lease of life (although a rather degrading one in the eyes of the old tars) right up to the First World War.

Cheap and plentiful though they were, tank sailers were by no means ideal tonnage for oil, and very few were purpose-built from scratch after 1886. True, the double-containment method offered considerable economies over package shipments through bulk handling; but paying carrying capacity was still lost through the weight of the second container, the permanent metal tanks, and the dead space both between the tanks and the side of the vessel and under the "false bottom" on which the tanks rested. Tank sailers also tended to handle badly in high seas or strong winds, rolling excessively, and were therefore never a completely successful solution for Atlantic oil shipping.

The real and lasting solution to deepsea oil transport only came when steam became viable as a means of propulsion for tankers, and when improved metal construction and rivetting techniques finally allowed the shippers to do away with the wasteful double-containment method.

Steam ships were already in use on the Caspian, but only became economic for cheap bulk cargoes like oil on the longer Atlantic route during the 1880s. Steam was by no means a new idea for marine propulsion. The Watt engine had been the subject of considerable experiment for water transport for at least 100 years, starting with unambitious adaptations of small river craft on both sides of the Atlantic. The first recorded commercial steamship in the US was in 1807 and in Europe in 1812, in the UK. These early experiments needed a lot of work done on them to make them commercially viable. In America this was done on rivers using wood for bunkers, but Europe, and particularly Britain, soon found that steam fired by coal could help supply its important demand for short-haul deepsea transport, around its coast and to and from the Continent. Britain took the natural lead in this development partly because of her powerful position in seafaring and shipbuilding, and partly because of Scotland's strength in engineering.

Steam in its early days, however, was not an economic proposition for long voyages. The engine and coal bunkers, though excellent on land for industrial purposes, took up a totally uneconomic proportion of a vessel's carrying capacity. The longer the journey, the more uneconomic it became. The less visionary amongst the traditional shipping industry firmly believed that steam would never catch on or compete favourably with sail. It did, however, have one saving grace: it guaranteed regularity, a highly desirable feature for the carriage of valuable cargoes such as passengers and mail. No longer were sailing and arrival times at the mercy of the elements and tides. Britain was the first of many nations to recognise the benefit of this and to introduce special mail subsidies which enabled regular steam services to be established from

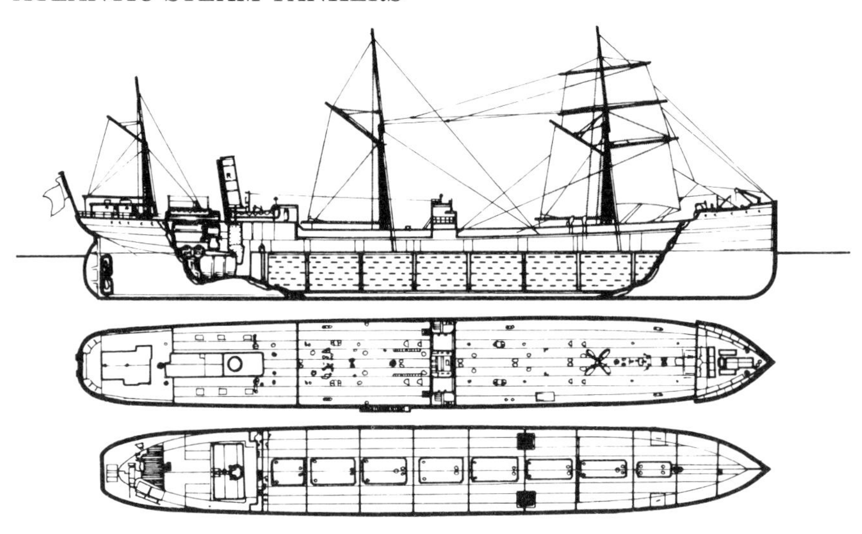

"Gluckauf", 1886 built by Armstrong Whitworth with the location of engine room aft separated from the cargo space by the pump room forming a cofferdam. A double bottom was only included underneath the engine room space. The "Gluckauf" is the prototype of the tanker as we know it today.

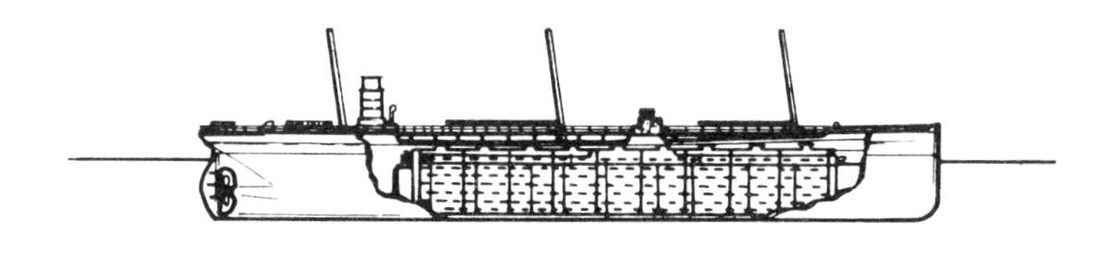

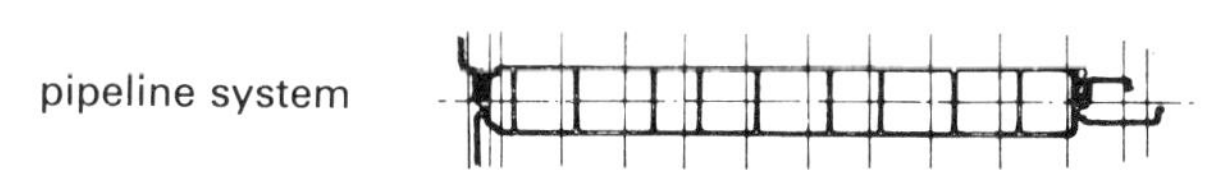

"Bayonne", 1889 built by A. & J. Inglis Ltd. of Glasgow, UK, for the British Subsidiary of Standard Oil, the Anglo-American Oil Co. in 1888 carrying capacity of some 4,000 tons, loaded speed 11.85 knots and traded between the U.S.A. and England. Note the engine room is aft as with the "Gluckauf".

1840. The cost to the governments concerned was considerable and no private company was prepared to invest similar amounts to transport low value goods. Deliveries of such goods had always been erratic and buyers would not pay a premium to guarantee regular arrivals. This situation prevailed until 1865, when the introduction of the compound engine (or twin expansion chamber) effected a dramatic reduction in coal consumption and hence bunker space. Fifteen years later, in 1880, the triple expansion engine offered a further improvements so substantial that for the first time the steam engine became a viable economic means of propulsion for all types of cargo, including oil in direct competition with sail.

Suddenly then in the 1880s, by chance rather than by design, it became possible for the stronger European oil importers, encouraged by the new-found atmosphere of security created by Standard Oil, to invest in superior steam-powered vessels. Meanwhile, metal construction techniques had also been improving gradually. For several years, iron riveted tankers had proved their worth on the Caspian, and by the mid-1880s more courageous European shippers were prepared to entrust oil to a single metal hull structure even in the much greater stresses of the Atlantic. Even so, the risks of iron-hulled, steam driven tankers could not be underestimated. The power unit was fuelled by open coal boilers, not a happy marriage to a dangerous cargo like oil, especially in a leaky contrivance such as the 19th century riveted hull. Dangers were increased by the motion of bulk oil on the high seas, which could surge and slop around very violently. These effects were cut down by installing transverse and longitudinal bulkheads but even so there was still a deeprooted fear in many owners minds that rivets might open up in mid-Atlantic and the vapours reach the boilers.

The first genuine attempt to overcome these fears and difficulties and to build a deepsea steamship adapted to oil, and oil alone, using only the hull as the oil container, was the *Gluckauf* built in 1886 in Newcastle upon Tyne, England, by Armstrong Mitchell & Co. for Mr. Heinrich Riedemann of the German subsidiary of the Standard. A year earlier, Riedemann had had the composite ship *Andromeda* converted in the States to carry 3,000 tons of oil in 72 tanks, 24 on each of the three decks. Trade on the New York to Germany run was expanding fast. The *Gluckauf* was not just a one-off venture, but part of the overall expansion policy of the Standard in Europe.

The *Gluckauf* had her keel laid at the Walker yard on November 25th, 1885 and was launched on June 16th, 1886. She could carry 2,975 tons of kerosine and was around 3,500 DWT; fully riveted throughout and, unlike the Caspian tankers, with her triple-expansion steam engine at the stern where it would interfere least with her cargo. Although more advanced than the Caspian vessels in many respects, it is certain that she evolved out of the designs used for the inland sea. Henry Swan of Armstrong Mitchell had already built a few years earlier the *Massis*, the *Poseidon* and the *Armeniak* for the Caspian. It is also likely that Swan visited Molata on his way to Russian some time earlier.

The *Gluckauf* was certainly revolutionary. So much so that when she arrived in New York to load, the long shoremen, oil workers and coopers immediately blacked her. They realised that her fast and automated loading systems would put them out of a job, so they persuaded the local coal merchants not to refuel her. Having arrived on the 30th July 1886, loaded her cargo, but no bunkers, she was forced on 6th August to sail up to St. John's where she refuelled. Twenty days later she arrived safely at Geestermunde in Germany with her first cargo. As a result of this unhappy start to her life, she had additional bunker capacity fitted so she did not have to bunker in New York. However this does not seem have been been her only problem, for while her name translated means "Good luck", she was soon nicknamed *Fleigauf* or "Blow up" – a good indication of the general faith in these early tankers.

Sure enough, there continued to be a number of tragic losses, just as there had been with tank sailers. Again not always the designers' fault, for there was the engineer who put his lamp into a hatch when ballasting to see how much water had been taken on board. As was said at the time . . . "the ship was lost, and himself, too, poor fellow". The *Gluckauf* lasted until 1893 when she was wrecked off Long Island, but her sistership only lasted three years before being lost, and a great many other early tankers were destroyed by fire or lost without trace in mid-Atlantic. It was, therefore, many years before owners became totally confident of the single containment system; and to some extent this explains the popularity of double-containment tank steamers, as well as the tank sailers, into the early 20th century.

It was not a simple transition to take the tried and tested designs of the Caspian ships and put them on the North Atlantic. In part it was bound to be trial and error. Not only did the designers not know how the winter seas would affect tankers, but they could not anticipate all the mistakes that the crews would make in operating this completely new class of vessel. The dangers of the heavy Atlantic seas were soon appreciated and designs amended accordingly by fitting more transverse bulkheads, reducing each tank size and the potential movement of the cargo. However, if the master mishandled the ship resulting in plates being buckled or rivets loosened, he, rather than any design deficiency, was considered at fault. And in many cases he was.

There was one master who overballasted his 4,000 DWT tanker in mid-ocean by a mere 2,000 tons of sea water, causing very severe straining in every compartment. Another, who forgot to open his vent valves when deballasting, succeeded in creating such a vacuum in the tanks that he lowered the ship's tank top by three inches. However, the argument that "if ships are not strong enough, they should be made stronger" was gradually got through over the years to the builders.

The natural reluctance on the part of many owners to move to tankers did not stop many others investing in the new style of bulk oil carrier and from 1886, the world's deepsea tanker fleet began to grow rapidly. Each year saw improvements in safety, performance, size and economy, so that by the end of the century 8,000 DWT tankers were the norm and, by the First World War, 12,000 DWT. Size was in fact a major factor in the rapid dominance of steam over sail. The sailing ship was inherently limited by spars, sails, and sheer handling ability. The beautiful clipper, however large and efficient compared with earlier sailing ships, had taken the physical development of sail just about as far as it could go. Although metal hulled clippers of up to 10,000 DWT were built, these were the exception. For the steam tanker it easily became the rule.

As size increased, the location of the power unit had to be reconsidered. To begin with, builders followed the example of the *Gluckauf* with superstructure amidships and the power unit in the stern, keeping the boilers and the oil cargo as far away from each other as possible, and "minimising the danger of sparks from the funnel falling on the deck". However, as size increased, the problem of trimming a tanker with engines in her stern became greater. So they were placed amidships, where they allowed higher speed (and hence demanded less bunker capacity), and where they were structurally safer. There were certain disadvantages to resiting the engines. Extra cofferdams and two pump rooms were needed, an oiltight tunnel had to be built to house the tail shaft as it passed under the stern tanks (an unwelcome additional expense), and the centre-line bulkhead was no longer continuous. However, on balance, the central position was favoured and the tanker funnel moved from the stern to the superstructure amidships, as with all other types of steam shipping of the time.

The steam tanker offered freight at around 25% cheaper than parcel shipments; expensive handling could be minimised and paying cargo maximised; and costly packaging materials for barrels and tins no longer had to be shipped out to refineries to make up the export containers. One major economic and operational disadvantage remained – oil trades were all one-way. Unlike the general cargo ship, the specialist tanker could not take paying cargo on the return voyage. To overcome this many tankers during the late 19th century were designed to carry general cargo as well. The oil tank openings were large and the tanks themselves could be steam-cleaned and well ventilated, allowing a wide range of commodities, from cloth to foodstuffs, to be shipped on what would otherwise be an expensive ballast voyage.

By the 20th century, the oil tanker in its various forms had become a standard type of ship, although there were still relatively few of them compared with other types of merchant shipping. In many ways these early ships looked very similar to the modern design, except for their cargo handling derricks and – a strange feature to the 20th century eye – sails. It was for many years normal practice to carry auxiliary sails on steam tankers just in case the engine failed or there were not enough bunkers for the voyage – a fair indication of how unreliable and unsophisticated these early tankers still were.

6 RUSSIA AND THE FAR EAST

All major developments in oil shipping since the mid-1880s had been generated by European traders, either owned or sheltered by the "umbrella" of Standard Oil, and were directed towards improved bulk transport on the important Atlantic route. The Russians, even though the Caspian steam tankers had made history in the 1870s and early '80s, made little headway in deepsea shipping in the '80s and '90s. There was a small but steady stream of exports to Northern Europe via the Baltic, but the inland Caspian-Volga route dominated for most of the 19th century, simply because the alternative route to the open seas – to the Black Sea and on to the Mediterranean – was not yet properly developed. It was 1883 before there was a direct rail link – the Transcaucasian railroad to Batoum on the Black Sea; and 1905 before a 550-mile pipeline to Batoum direct from the Baku was completed – more than 20 years after the American equivalent to the East Coast.

The reasons for this delay were complex. America had a 10-year head start over the Russian industry; but more important, the Black Sea link was against the interests of the all-powerful Nobels, who controlled the alternative Caspian Sea/Volga inland route, and who therefore contrived to keep prices on this route low enough to discourage investment in the railroad. The pipeline was against the interests of the Russian government who stood to lose the very high monopolistic profits they made on the Transcaucasian railroad once it had been built. At the same time, Russia's producing regions were so inaccessible, her main markets so diverse and hinterland-oriented, that refineries, unlike those in America, had to remain source-located at Baku. Bulk terminals on the Black Sea therefore had to be built up purely on the volume of seaborne exports, either to feed tank ships or the tinning factories which were established there, and this took time.

Since the railway link to Batoum was only single track, rising to 3,000 feet, with a maximum gradient of 1 in 22, little over 100,000 tons per year of oil could be delivered to the Black Sea. Labour facilities at Batoum were inadequate for large deepsea vessels. Cargo handling was bad with a high frequency of damage to barrels, many of which were non-standard sizes and stowed badly.

By the turn of the century, Russia at last achieved a good distribution network to the open seas, influenced not by the Nobels but by a French family, the Rothschilds. They had become involved in financing the Transcaucasian railway which the Nobels opposed, and encouraged to enter the Russian oil industry by the independent producers and refiners who wanted to break the suffocating monopoly of the Nobels during the 1880s. The Rothschilds invested in all sectors of the industry and soon overtook the Nobels as the major southern exporter. The Nobels maintained control of exports from the Baltic.

Had the Black Sea route been opened up 10 or 20 years before, it would have enjoyed great export potential not only to Europe but to many other parts of the world. In practice, it came far too late to compete in most international routes against the by now enormous strength of the Standard empire which had spread its tentacles all over the world. The Russians had to be content with the southern European market plus some long-haul trades to the East. There was some precedent for the latter since there had been a constant "trickle" of Russian oil to the East since 1885, when it reached India, and 1888, when it reached the Far East. This inferior position in the main international markets largely explains the lack of Russian influence on tanker design and developments after the *Zoraster* period. Initially, Black Sea exports were in small sailing ships which had become virtually a thing of the past on the Atlantic, mostly owned by Greeks but also by Norwegians. However, tankers soon appeared on the Mediterranean, around the same time as on the Atlantic, initially chartered to and later owned by the Rothschilds. In 1885, the tank ship *Sviet* was built for the Russian Steam Navigation Co. in Sweden and began regularly trading between Batoum and North European ports in 1886, while the *Bakuin* of 2,550 DWT, a true tanker, was launched the day after the *Gluckauf*, also to trade to the UK and Continent. Although the giant Russian oil industry failed to capture any large markets outside Europe from the Standard, one small independent British trader did – using Russian oil. Marcus Samuel, founder of Shell and eventually a partner in the great Royal Dutch/Shell Group. M. Samuel & Co traded to the Far East: exporting coal and importing a variety of Eastern Commodities, notably exotic shells, back to Victorian England. Samuel, recognising the great potential for petroleum

STEAM TANKERS FOR THE FAR EAST

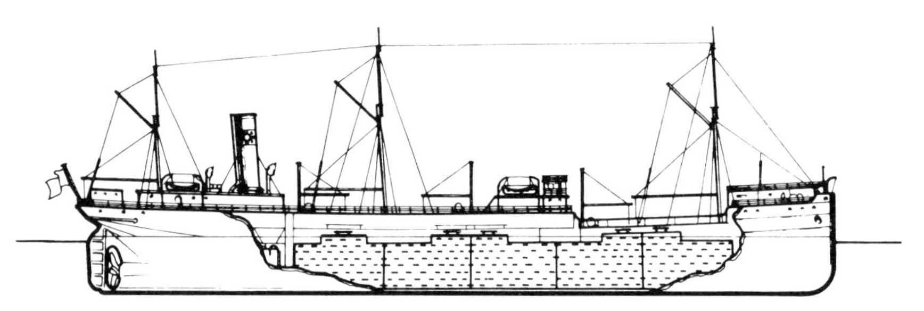

The "Murex" built 1892 for the Shell Transport and Trading Co. (UK) was the first vessel to carry bulk oil through Suez, making this historic voyage from Batum to Singapore and Bangkok in 1892—5010 DWT. Note general cargo derricks.

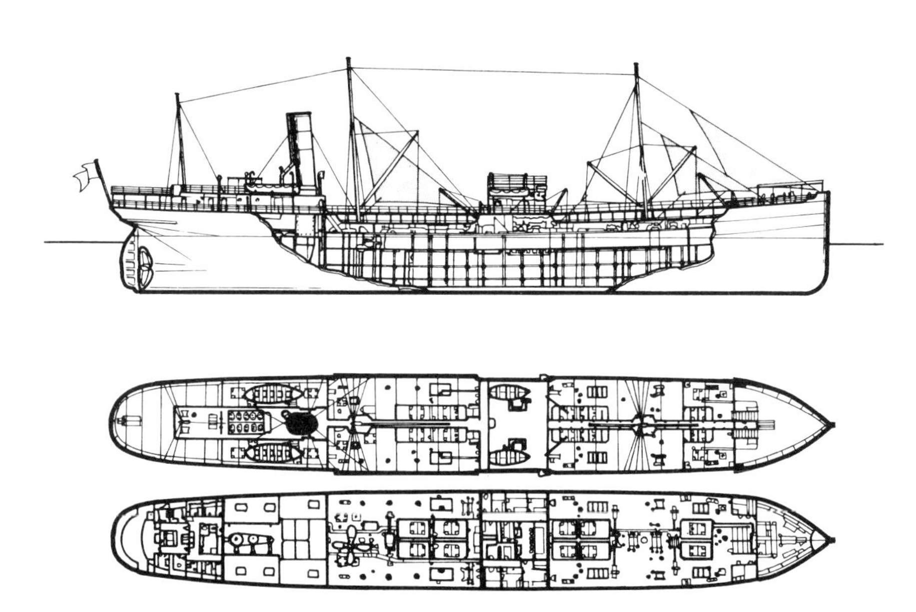

The s.s. "Sultan van Langkat", the first real deep sea tanker of the Royal Dutch built 1898 for trading in eastern waters. Note general cargo derricks.

exports in a part of the world he knew well, planned to do what no other trader had achieved – break the power of the Standard in the Far East.

Although by the 1890s most of the Standard's East Coast exports to Europe were being transported in steam tankers, all Far East shipments were still going in sailing ships, in cans and cases. The alternative route via the Suez Canal had been barred to tank ships when the Canal was opened in 1869. The authorities had quite rightly banned bulk oil shipments as being unsafe for such a waterway. Although parcel shipments could equally well have used the Suez Canal since the authorities had allowed case oils through from the start, it was not worth it. The winds were by no means as good as via the Cape. The Cape route, on the other hand, was not well served with bunkering stations, so here sailing ships had to be used. Even so, the Cape route under sail was by no means ideal. In 1890 Standard requested special permission for its tankers to use the Suez Canal. The authorities refused on the grounds that, while tanker design had become safer in the 20 years since the Canal had opened, Standard's vessels were old and not safe enough.

It was here that Marcus Samuel saw his chance of beating the Standard at its own game. If he could acquire a cheap, reliable supply of oil and then develop a tanker which would be acceptable to the Suez authorities, he could ship bulk oil supplies to the Far East through the Canal and reduce the delivered price to such a level that even the Standard could not follow its traditional strategy against potentially dangerous competition. Samuel would be spared the savage price wars which had forced the opposition either to go bust or to sell out to the Standard at a knock-down price. Samuel secured the oil from the Rothschilds in Russia, to be loaded in the Black Sea. The tanker, he specifically designed, in great secrecy, to allay the fears of the Suez Canal Authorities.

In 1892, his new design, incorporating the special water ballast tanks, which could be deballasted in case the tanker went aground in the Canal, two cofferdams (twin bulkheads with an empty space between them) – one at each end of the cargo tanks – and an oiltight centre bulkhead, was accepted for transit in a loaded condition through the Canal – in the face of considerable opposition from "unknown parties". It is a moot point whether the Authorities, being of course British, were in fact more influenced by the new design or by the fact that Samuel was British and his ships British-built, running under British flag and for a British company! Everyone was happy with this new arrangement (except Welsh tin miners who suddenly lost an important market for their wares since Russian oil could now be tinned in the Far East rather than Batoum as was the case until 1892). The Standard's vessels were still banned. In fact many earlier tankers did not have cofferdams or oiltight centre bulkheads. It was not that the Standard's tankers were sub-standard, just that tanker design was continually evolving. The Suez requirements were just one step in this process. However, this was little comfort to the Standard. To add insult to injury, the Standard had to continue shipping cases around Africa in sailing ships with the result that its tins were often rusty on arrival. Samuel's

MAJOR WORLD SEABORNE OIL MOVEMENTS – 1885

(Total 1.9 million tons per year)

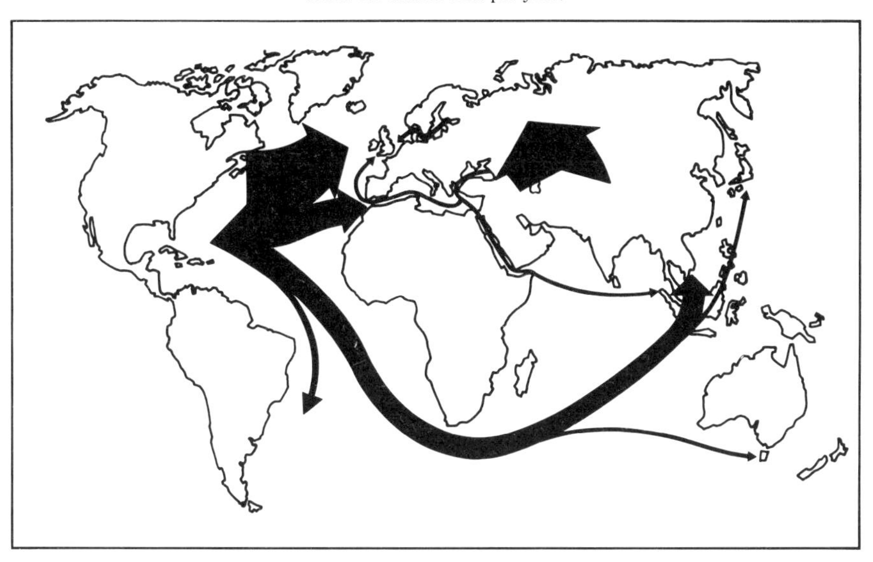

MAJOR WORLD OIL SHIPPING TRADES – 1885

(Total 350,000 tons of oil carrying capacity)

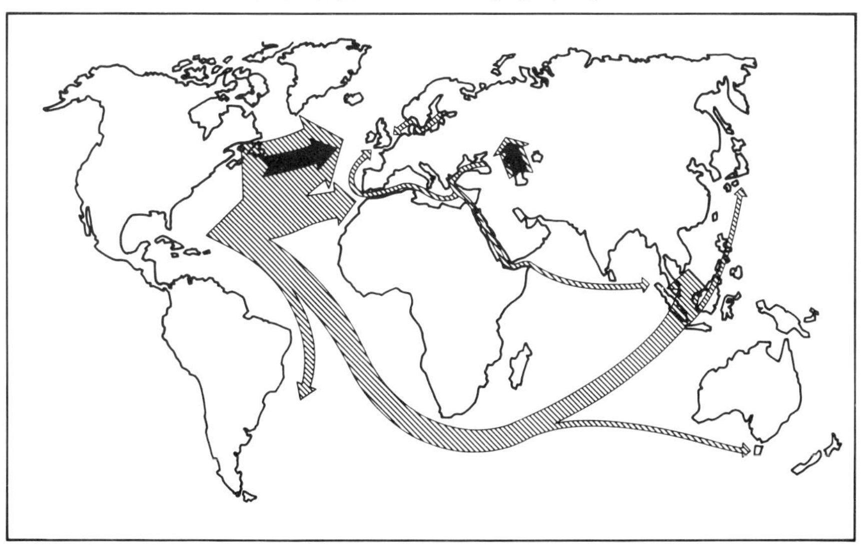

KEY TO MAPS:

Bulk oil shipping (steam tankers and tank sailers)

Case and barrel oilshipping (general cargo and sailing ships)

made in the Far East were bright and new. The Standard therefore, lost a significant market share through Samuel to Russian oil.

Samuel's first tanker through the Suez Canal was the 5,010 DWT *Murex* – named, as all his tankers were, after shells. She loaded Baku kerosine, the only product allowed through Suez at this stage, at Batoum, towed through and discharged at Singapore and Bangkok. As late as 1902, Shell tried to ship gasoline via Suez in the *Murex* from the East to the UK, only to be refused permission. He had to turn her back and sail around the Cape instead. The Suez Authorities did not allow gasoline via the Canal in bulk until 1907, fearing for this highly dangerous cargo in the heat. The kerosine trade alone, however, allowed Samuel to build up a sizeable fleet of good class British ships. Like many Atlantic tankers, they carried not only oil but also dry cargo. On the return voyage from the East, tanks were cleaned with specially installed steam equipment and loaded with goods such as sugar, rice and tapioca. Through this precedent it became the acknowledged practice among Far East owners in the late 19th century to design their tankers to carry dry cargo shipments as well.

By 1897, Samuel's oil sideline had become so important that he formed "the Shell Transport and Trading Company", named after his original trade. Ten years later in 1907, Shell joined forces with the Royal Dutch Company for the Working of Petroleum Wells in the Dutch East Indies, a Dutch oil development company which had rapidly grown to become the largest producer in the Far East. So was formed the major oil company we know today, and one of the most important oil shippers of that time.

7 EMERGENCE OF A WORLD PATTERN

Throughout the 19th century, the specialist oil carrying fleet was tied almost exclusively to specific trades, owned or operated by the oil companies who controlled these trades. And the number of trades was significantly limited by the fact that only two production areas – America and Russia – accounted for at least 94% of world crude oil production, obviously limiting international export patterns. Oil had been discovered in commercial quantities and developed in Canada, the Dutch East Indies, India, Peru and Western Europe. However, at the turn of the century none of these areas showed any real significance in world terms. The East Coast of America and the Baku in Russia retained their joint monopoly of world refining capacity and the vast majority of seaborne exports continued to be from the East Coast and the Black Sea.

By far the most important deepsea oil route during the 19th century was across the Atlantic. From nil in 1860, volumes rose to 1.2 million tons per year in 1885 and to 2.3m tons in 1900. The trade in the first 25 years was overwhelmingly kerosine in parcel shipments; by 1885, out of the 1,000 or so vessels trading in oil on the Atlantic, there were only a handful of 'bulk' oil carriers, these all being double-containment tank ships. However, although they only represented about 1% of actual vessels in use, they accounted for something like 10% of total oil carrying capacity because of their larger size and higher trading efficiency. By the turn of the century, a completely different picture had emerged. Trade had doubled since 1885 and there were over 60 steam tankers in use on the Atlantic, representing over 80% of the total Atlantic fleet. Parcel shipment on the same run had dwindled to under 1%, the remainder being bulk oil in tank sailers or steamers.

Virtually all these new tankers were owned and run by European companies – chiefly controlled by the Standard. Standard's British affliate, Anglo America Oil Co. Ltd, was the major shipowner in the group, acquiring seven new tankers between 1886 and 1890 and another 13 between 1890 and 1900. By 1909, it owned 28 tankers, 15 sailing ships and four steam cargo ships for case oil. The next largest in the group was the German affliate, Deutsch-Amerikanisch Petroleum Ges, owning eight tankers by 1880 and another 13 by 1900. These two, together with the Dutch affiliate, owned 46 steam tankers by 1900, or around half the total tanker tonnage in the world. Their fleets had included vessels such as the *Gluckauf*, and *Vaderland* which were owned as just another asset. The Standard itself, under American flag, owned a number of tank sailers but virtually no tankers.

The only other major export outlet for American oil was the Far East. This route accounted for 0.3 million tons in 1885 and 0.4m in 1900, approximately 10% of American oil exports. On this long but good trade wind route around the Cape of Good Hope, big fast clippers, pushed out of so many other trades by the steamship, found employment. On other less important long-haul package routes, such as to Australasia or parts of South America, the clipper also thrived. Bulk oil shipments gradually forced their way into these trades during the beginning of the next century and vicious battles often developed between bulk and case oils. On both sides of the Atlantic, smaller sailing ships of around 200 tons continued to be used on short coastal routes.

By comparison with the Standard empire which controlled virtually all America's seaborne exports, Russian interests had a minimal stake in the world's deepsea tanker fleet. This was because, unlike America which in 1900 exported 50% of her production on deepsea routes, Russia exported less than 20% by sea: two short haul routes from the Black Sea to Southern Europe and from the Baltic to North West Europe, plus the long-haul trades to the East via Suez. However, on all these routes, it was foreign controlled companies who owned almost all the tanker tonnage. In 1885, Atlantic movements were 10 times as great as those out of Russia. By 1900, with the growing diversification of US production plus the fact that Russia had overtaken America in total oil production, the importance of Russian deepsea exports was increasing to around half the Atlantic trade.

By contrast, the inland Caspian-Volga link to the northern overland route always carried enormous volumes of oil – larger even than the Atlantic trade. The Caspian fleet had started off, in the 1870s and '80s, being highly sophisticated: as early as 1885, when there were only about 10 tank sailers and no tankers in use on the Atlantic, half the Caspian oil carrying capacity was converted schooners, and a third steam tankers or tank ships like the *Zoraster*. The Caspian fleet, however, did not develop in the mainstream of oil shipping after the 1880s, simply because it served different needs and did not have to contend with deepsea conditions. By 1900, there were 129 tank steamers in use on the Caspian – at around 1,000 DWT considerably smaller than the by now common 8,000 tonner on the Atlantic – together with some 212 converted schooners, around 1,500 wooden and metal-hulled bulk oil barges, plus case oil carriers on both the Caspian and the Volga. By 1906 this had become 131 tank steamers and 149 schooners. The vast majority of this shipping was owned or controlled by the Nobels.

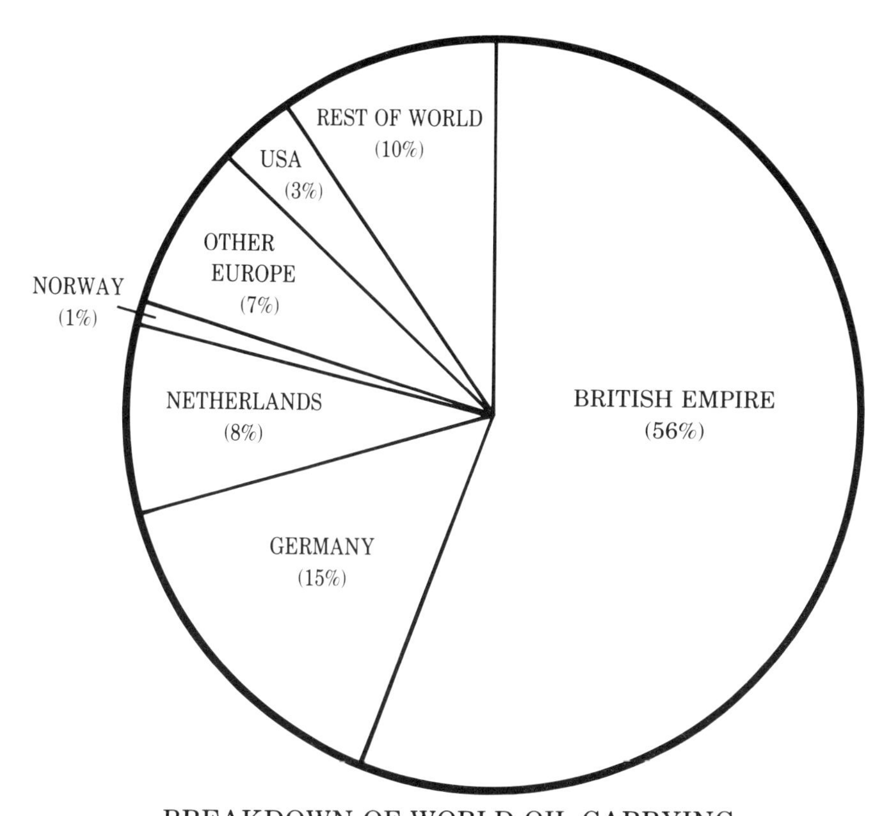

BREAKDOWN OF WORLD OIL CARRYING
FLEET BY FLAG IN 1900
(Steam tankers, oil sailing ships and barges over 500 GRT)

Most of these Caspian tank steamers were built many thousands of miles away from this inland sea, in Germany, Russia itself, Britain and, of course, Sweden. How did they get into the Caspian? The most tortuous route had to be taken via the myriad of rivers, lakes and canals connecting the Baltic and the Caspian. The canal locks presented major limitations on the size of vessel and two standard hull sizes developed. One with just under a 28 feet beam, fitted exactly into the smallest lock, the other more than 150 in length, had to be built in sections. These larger tank ships were bolted together to sail to the Baltic, then separated into their two halves to be permantly riveted together once they were in the Caspian. The depth of six feet of water on these inland waterways was also a problem. All dispensable removable parts were shipped separately and pontoons fitted under the engine room to give extra buoyancy.

From St. Petersburg (now Leningrad) on the Baltic, up the River Neva and through the Marinsky Canal, they moved eventually on to the Volga and, after some 2,500 miles, into the Caspian.

The only other Russian oil tanker trade of major significance during the 19th Century was Marcus Samuel's Suez route. The length of this voyage, from Baku to the Far East, was over twice the Atlantic run and Samuel's need for tankers was therefore sizeable: by 1900, Shell owned 27 tankers, some of them small 500 DWT vessels for trading in the Far East, but 15 were around 6,000 DWT and specially designed for the Suez voyage. This put Shell second only to the Standard (with 60 tankers on the Atlantic) in tanker ownership at that time.

By 1900 the world deepsea tanker fleet had grown to a total of 109 vessels averaging 4,900 DWT – or a total of some 500,000 DWT, approximately the size of one of today's giant ULCCs. In addition there were the inland water fleets, as on the Caspian. Thanks to Marcus Samuel and to the shipowning policy of the Standard's European subsidiaries, British companies under British flags owned 56% of world tanker tonnage and all European companies under their respective flags nearly 90%. It is therefore not surprising that tankers continued to be built as well as owned in Europe. It had always been up to the European, the traditional merchant, to come and get American oil and the result of the Standard's "octopus" policies was to leave the shipbuilding and owning initiative in its traditional place rather than concentrating it in America. In any case, American shipyards had become blinkered by their success with the clipper and while European yards were building larger and larger steam ships, they were building larger and larger clippers.

Of course, Britain, and the rest of Europe for that matter, had had the advantage of two centuries of highly discriminatory shipping policies, by which they had excluded foreign flags from their own captive colonial trades. By the end of the 18th century, Britain had become the world's greatest colonial power, gaining most from these policies, and so had become the greatest shipowning and building nation in the world. The era of free trade which came about in the middle of the 19th century allowed other maritime nations to

OIL SHIPPING CAPACITY ON MAIN WORLD SEA ROUTES 1885 AND 1900

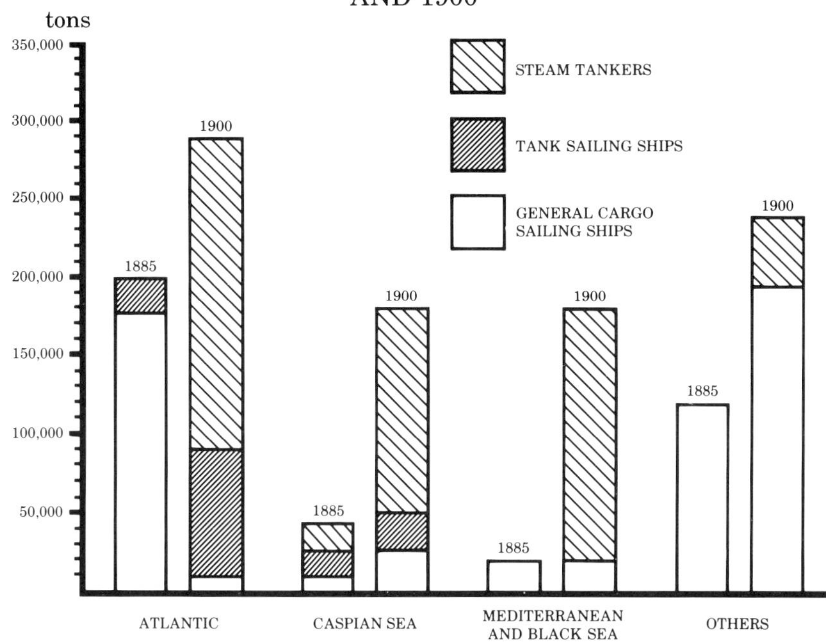

participate in a fairer share of merchant trade, but countries such as the recently freed colony of America had a long way to go to catch up with the experience, wealth and technology of British yards, registration and owners. Although American light industry had overtaken British knowhow by the turn of the century, heavy industry lagged well behind British steel and engineerings skills. American yards were, therefore, slow in developing a sophisticated maritime engineering and tool industry in the late 19th century, with the result that they were late in building metal hulled sailing ships. In 1900, around 50% of all steam tankers had been built in British yards, 30% in other European yards and only 20% in American yards, and many of these had to have their boilers imported from Britain, due to the lack of domestic technology.

Because Standard Oil, Samuel and the Russian producers all had their tankers tied into substantially captive trades on their main oil routes, the 19th century produced virtually no tanker market. Oil companies owned over 90% of all steam tankers and with the bulk of these on relatively fixed employment, there was little demand for cross-chartering. Where it did occur, it was almost exclusively between importing and exporting oil traders or between affiliates of the Standard Group. The power of the Standard was so great that it physically deterred independent owners from buying tankers, since it could, if it wanted, ensure that they had no employment. Those independents that did buy tankers were sometimes forced to become involved in oil trading to ensure employment of their vessels, and so lost their status as independent owners.

The only large independently-owned group of oil carrying vessels were the general cargo sailing ships. It was here that there was a spot market to charter oil tonnage, not in bulk, but in barrels and cases. However, because oil was not the safest of cargo and especially because it was always difficult to get rid of the smell of oil, particularly in a wooden ship, British owners tended to keep out of this trade, preferring the more lucrative and cleaner general cargo business. Very few British tramps were involved in barrel and tin oil shipments. As oil companies themselves owned many case oil sailing ships, this sector of oil traffic was not the exclusive province of the independents.

Barrels, cases, tanks, tankers . . . sailers and steamers . . . wood, iron and steel. The second half of the 19th century was a period of great change. Not only in how to carry the new commodity of oil at sea, but also how to build and power ships. Oil itself was beginning to have a major impact on the world in general and, one way or another, on the design of tankers. This was the birth and the childhood of the modern tanker industry. The painful period of evolution had occurred, but even by 1900 there was still a long way to go before the tanker was to become what we know today as a bulk oil carrier.

BOOK II
SOUTH TO THE CARIBBEAN
(1900–1938)

An alternative cargo for the 8228BRT Soviet tanker *Sovetskaya Neft.* Soya beans being offloaded by a wheat crane at Hamburg.

8 THE RISE OF AMERICA, THE FALL OF EUROPE

Even in 1900, oil was still an insignificant source of energy in most parts of the world. It represented only some 2.5% of world energy consumption; the degree of importance of, say, nuclear power today. Tankers, on the other hand, fared even worse in world terms – just 1.5% of total merchant tonnage. Most shipping was the all-purpose general cargo vessel or passenger ship, not highly specialised vessels like the tanker.

By 1938, oil had risen to account for 26% of world energy use, while tankers had become a strong and vital part of world shipping. In these early years of the new century, the tanker fleet grew from 0.5 million DWT to 16.1m DWT or to 16% of world tonnage – 10 times as important as in 1900.

The turn of the century was a watershed for both the oil and tanker worlds. As the 19th century ended, so did the dominance of European industrial power and that of America began to take over. For the USA, the 20th century brought mass production for mass markets; for Europe it brought mass destruction and mass killing. The focal point of the oil industry and tankers moved decisively across the Atlantic to the Americas, where it stayed firmly until after the Second World War.

Throughout the 19th century, the USA had increased its territories to become the nation we know today. At the beginning of the century it was just a group of eastern seaboard states. By 1867, through acquisition, or annexation, it had absorbed Florida, the Gulf States, the mid-West and all the lands west of the Rockies. With the Civil War of the 1860s over, the latter years of the century were spent on consolidation and growth, so that by 1900, the USA was the foremost industrial power in the world and, by the First World War, accounted for more than a third of the world's industrial output.

The rate of development of the USA's industrial base and technology was staggering. Added to this was her fantastic natural wealth of minerals and agricultural lands, immigrant skills from Europe and, of course, oil. Until the end of the Second World War, all the major discoveries of oil were to be made in the Western Hemisphere* and, in particular, in the USA itself. As the political and economic power of the USA grew, so did her influence throughout the world and especially within the Western Hemisphere. It was not just her domestic discoveries which the USA controlled, but many of these new overseas finds, to the considerable consternation of the Old World across the Atlantic. With this not inconsiderable base of domestic and foreign oil gained so early in the century, the USA controlled, directly within her own frontiers or indirectly abroad through her oil companies, between 60% and 80% of total world oil production from the 1900s right through to the 1970s.

The wealth to be gained by exploiting the world's oil reserves was the USA's and she used it. As the world became more and more reliant upon oil, so the industrial and economic power of the USA rose and that of the British Empire, based on coal, crumbled and died.

At the turn of the century coal had been, and still was both economic and military power. Kerosine played a useful role in the illuminating market, but other oil products, like fuel oil, were no threat to coal. Only a few markets next to some of the oil wells themselves – in the Caspian and the Far East – had accepted fuel oil, and this was due more to the lack of coal supplies than anything else. Coal still fired the railways on land, the steam engines and furnaces of industry and the steam ship at sea. These markets – industry and transportation – were the big ones. It was these which oil had yet to penetrate.

It had been Britain, back in the 16th century, which had first developed coal and in the 19th century had the largest known reserves of high quality coal. She was also the largest exporter of coal. By the early 20th century, Britain controlled and shipped 75% of world seaborne coal trade. With this power over certain key commodities and sea lanes, it was not coincidence that the British Empire dominated the world in other respects. Coal had helped to make Britain great, and, on the high seas, the British Navy ruled the waves. Coal had been Britain's prime export for over 300 years, and the mainstay of the British tramp fleet.

By 1920, the picture had begun to change. Oil was now capturing many of coal's traditional markets both on land and at sea. And it was no longer Britain, or even Europe, controlling this growing force, but the USA.

*Western Hemisphere refers to North, Central and South America, plus the Caribbean islands.

There was only one other country with natural resources comparable to those of America, at that time, and that was Russia. However while American businessmen and Government rushed around at both home and abroad finding new oil, Russia reeled under the effects of the first major nationalisation seen in the oil industry. She could not even maintain her domestic output, let alone search for foreign oil. It was these crucial years that allowed America to get a grip on world oil, and Russia to lose her chance to control it.

The Russian Revolution came in 1917 to rock the world. Within three years, the Bolsheviks had invaded the Baku, nationalised the oil industry and crippled production. Output started to drop after the first ripples of discontent in 1905. By 1920, Russian oil had become almost entirely limited to internal use, as a result of Soviet policy cutting Russia off from her old trading partners. Very limited exports did return, but seaborne shipments from Russia never managed to account for more than 3% of world tanker trades. From being the birth place and the home of many of the early innovations in the tank ship and tanker, Russia – in one step – moved out of the story of tankers.

Western Europe and the Far East suddenly found they had to look for new sources of oil to replace the loss of Baku. Oil was to be found virtually all over the world, but the only new production of any real significance up to the end of the Second World War was in the Americas, and it was to the Western Hemisphere that the old purchasers of Russian oil had to turn.

Middle East oil was discovered as early as 1909, in Persia (Iran), but the development of these, and the other vast resources in the area, remained very limited until after the Second World War. Britain, through the Anglo-Persian Oil Company (founded in 1909, and later to be renamed the Anglo-Iranian Oil Company, then British Petroleum or BP), controlled most of this new Middle East production, but output was not sufficient to satisfy all her needs. Britain too had to look west for larger volumes of oil.

The plight of Western Europe, with its nearby supplies of oil cut off, was made considerably worse by the First and, for that matter, the Second World War. Between 1914 and 1918, Europe destroyed much of the wealth she had accumulated during past centuries. She could no longer afford to import whatever she wanted, and was forced to continue to depend upon her traditional coal industries. Not until after the Second World War, when she had also destroyed much of her coal industry, was Europe at last compelled to turn to oil.

After the First World War, the USA was consuming some 55% of world energy compared with Western Europe's 25%. Oil accounted for 20–30% of US energy consumption, but only some 10% in Western Europe. As a result, the USA was consuming around 60–70% of the world's total oil output between the wars. This was an incredible turn around from only 20 years earlier. In 1900 the USA had been taking only 20% of world oil and Europe over 50%. By 1920, not only had world production become centred on America, so had consumption.

WORLD CRUDE OIL PRODUCTION: 1900-1940

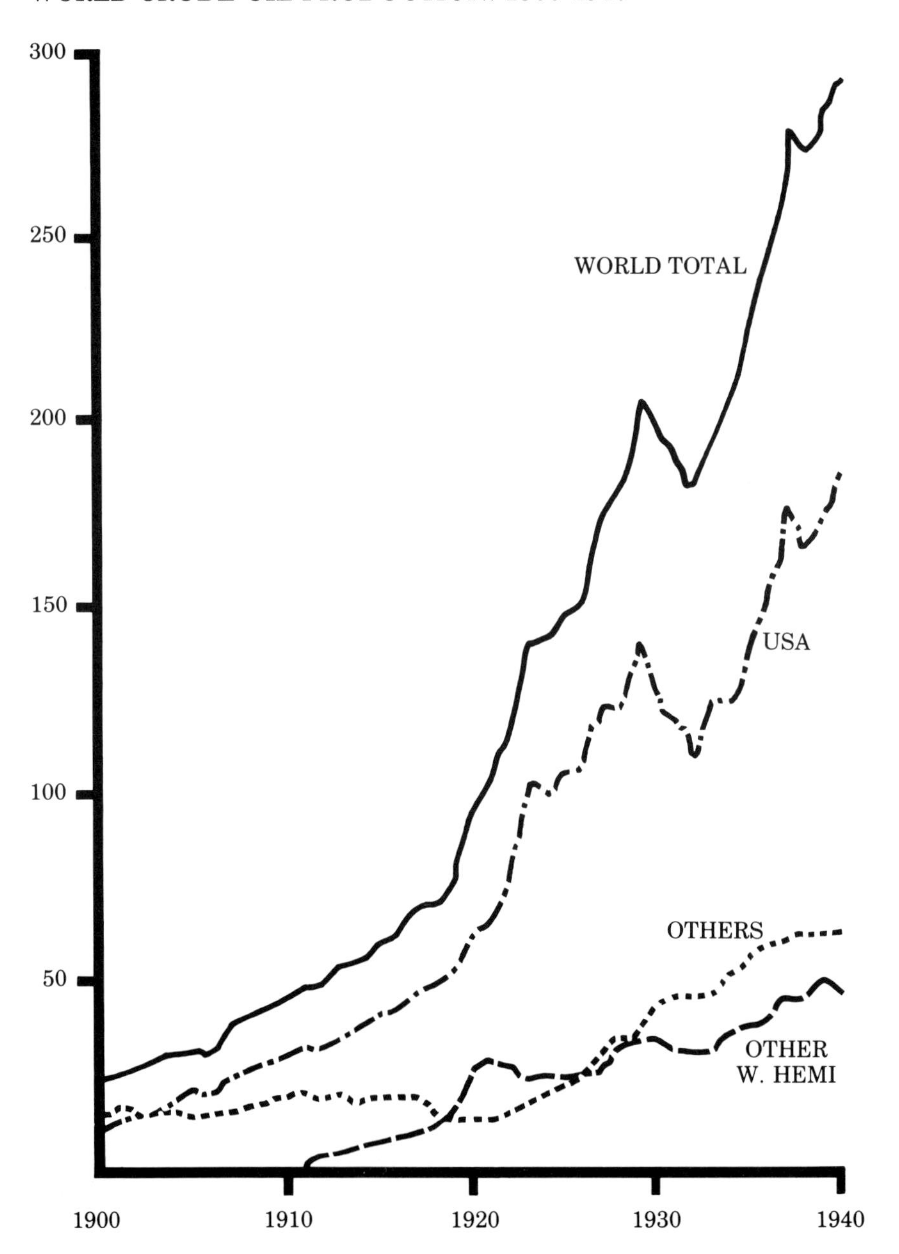

BREAKDOWN OF WORLD CRUDE OIL PRODUCTION

	USA	Mexico	Ven.	Other W. Hemi	Russia	Other E. Hemi	Total
1900	43%	—	—	1%	51%	5%	100%
1910	64%	1%	—	—	21%	14%	100%
1920	65%	23%	—	1%	4%	7%	100%
1930	62%	3%	10%	4%	9%	12%	100%
1940	63%	2%	9%	5%	10%	11%	100%

(W. Hemi covers all lands in North, Central and South America, plus the Caribbean.)

Between 1900 and 1938, world oil production leapt from 20 million tons per year to 273 million tons per year. At the turn of the century, Europe was producing 11 million tons per year, slightly more than the Western Hemisphere. By 1905, the Western Hemisphere's output had become 19 million tons per year, more than double that of Europe and from the Russian Revolution of 1917 until the Second World War its output grew to 10 times as much.

Tanker trades were forced to change as new production and export areas were created and old ones declined. The early years for tankers in the 19th century had been ones of relative peace and calm; no major external crises rocked the steady growth of either the oil or tanker worlds. What wars there were, such as the Franco-Prussian and Boer, had neither needed oil to fuel them nor had they disrupted the flow of oil. Even the American Civil War had very little effect. Oil had not grown large enough to become embroiled in world politics, or indeed in the meddling of politicians.

Within the oil and tanker industries, the growing strength of Rockefeller had ensured that there was planned and coordinated expansion. Tanker demand had developed undisturbed, allowing confidence to be built up and innovations, such as the steam engine, to be gradually tried, tested and phased into established trading patterns. But the 20th century was to be very different.

When Russia faded out of the picture, all the old sea trades from the Black Sea and Baltic dried up, to be replaced by greater volumes of exports from the Americas. Persia added a new loading zone and exported oil both to Western Europe via Suez, and to the Far East, but, even by 1938, that totalled only 9 million tons per year, just 7% of world seaborne oil movements. Following the First World War, with the rise of Persian exports and the decline of Black Sea shipments, oil trades through Suez switched from being predominantly southbound to being northbound. In the Far East, oil was still being produced, but never in huge quantities.

The Americas had risen to dominate tanker trades. By 1925, 85% of all deepsea liftings were in the Western Hemisphere and even 10 years later, the figure was 80%. Oil production, consumption and trade all centred on this half of the world. Except during the few years of the First World War, it was developments inside this hemisphere which were to have the greatest influence on the demand for tankers until the Second World War.

Fire on the famous Texan Spindletop oilfield.

The discovery of oil in Lake Maracaibo in 1917 changed the face of this farming region of Venezuela.

The first of the British 50,000-tonners, BP Tanker Company's *British Queen*.

9 OPENING UP THE US

The major oil producing states in the early 20th century were Texas and California. When Edwin Drake disovered oil in the north east in 1859, neither of these states had been part of the USA for much more than 10 years. In this huge country there were no direct railroad links from the south and west coasts to the sophisticated eastern seaboard and it is not surprising, therefore, that it took another 40 years to develop large oil fields in the new territories.

The Rocky Mountains were a natural barrier that few penetrated before the coming of the first transcontinental railroad link between east and west coasts, completed in 1869. The Californian gold rush of 1848 had created an enormous demand to get goods and people to the west, but most either had to make their way via the tortuous Cape Horn route, or transit via Panama or Nicaragua and on by sea to California. The overland pioneering Chisholm Trail offered only hardship and hostility and uncertain chance of arrival. This huge surge was a major force in the development of the American clipper. Demand continued throughout the century and even the new railroad was insufficient to satisfy it. Soon after this link was completed in the 1870s oil was discovered, but it was not until the 1900s that the big finds were to be made.

In the deep south, there was a further 10 year delay in finding oil. First production started in the 1880s again; it was not until the 1900s that there were significant finds. The development of the South lagged being the East Coast well beyond the Civil War of the 1860s. Inevitably the South lost the war, destroying the sophisticated and elitist society, built up around the plantations and slaves. The planters received no compensation when the slaves were freed and the slaves lost both homes and the only kind of permanent job available to them. It was to take decades for the South to recover and attract new blood.

By the new century, the United States was at last truly united and booming. Now even the farmers, so vital to the nation's welfare, were making good profits. Industrialists had huge and growing domestic markets at their feet, just waiting to be exploited. The scene was set for an unprecedented explosion in American wealth, and a growing demand for energy, "black gold" and the tanker.

In the 10 years from 1900 to 1910, US crude oil production jumped from 8.7m tons by 20 million tons a year. By the Second World War, it had reached 229.8m tons a year. It was during these first few years of the century that the American picture changed completely and set the pattern for the next 30 years. In 1900, the North Eastern states had produced 90% of total US crude, but by 1910, their portion fell to only 32%. Their importance steadily declined with the rise of other areas so that by the 1930s what had been the heart of American oil production, accounted for just some 5% of total output of US crude oil.

There were two big new producing areas. One was east of the Rockies in the Mid-Continent, running north from northern Texas some 500 miles into Kansas. The other was west of the Rockies in California. A third but not nearly as important a region was on the Gulf of Mexico coast, running east some 400 miles or more from the mouth of the Mississippi river in Louisiana into Texas. By the Second World War, the Mid-Continent had grown to account for 58% of the total US output, California 21% and the Gulf 15%.

These new production areas immediately created local markets which had previously been unable to afford to import oil from the East Coast: the South had not even developed from wood to coal. At the turn of the century, coal accounted for 71% of the total US energy market, wood 21%, natural gas 3%, hydroelectricity 3% and oil only 2%. The volumes of crude oil now being produced throughout the country were so large, particularly in the Mid-Continent and California, that more distant markets had to be found, and quickly. The US oil industry, was faced with the alternatives of having to create new overland transportation networks for land-locked crudes, or establish new shipping trades for excess coastal availability.

With oil being produced virtually throughout the US, most domestic markets could be satisfied out of crude supplies from either the same or a nearby state. The only area in real conflict was the highly populated and industrialised East Coast. Here demand had steadily grown, but production from the neighbouring North-East states had stagnated and even declined. The problem of oil transportation within this vast country was, therefore, simple to deduce, if not to solve. Any surplus oil in the Mid-Continent, the Gulf and California had to be got to the East Coast. What was left over could be exported.

BREAKDOWN OF U.S. TOTAL ENERGY CONSUMPTION

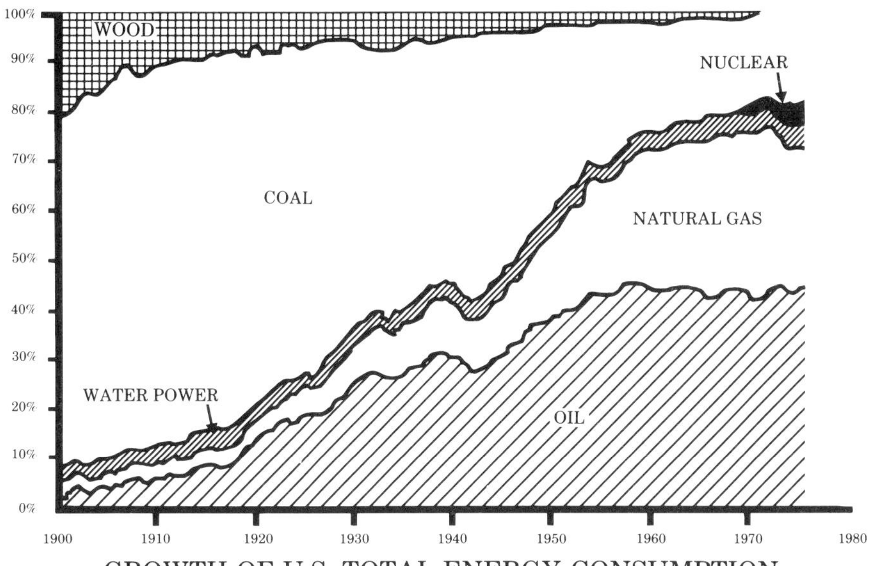

GROWTH OF U.S. TOTAL ENERGY CONSUMPTION

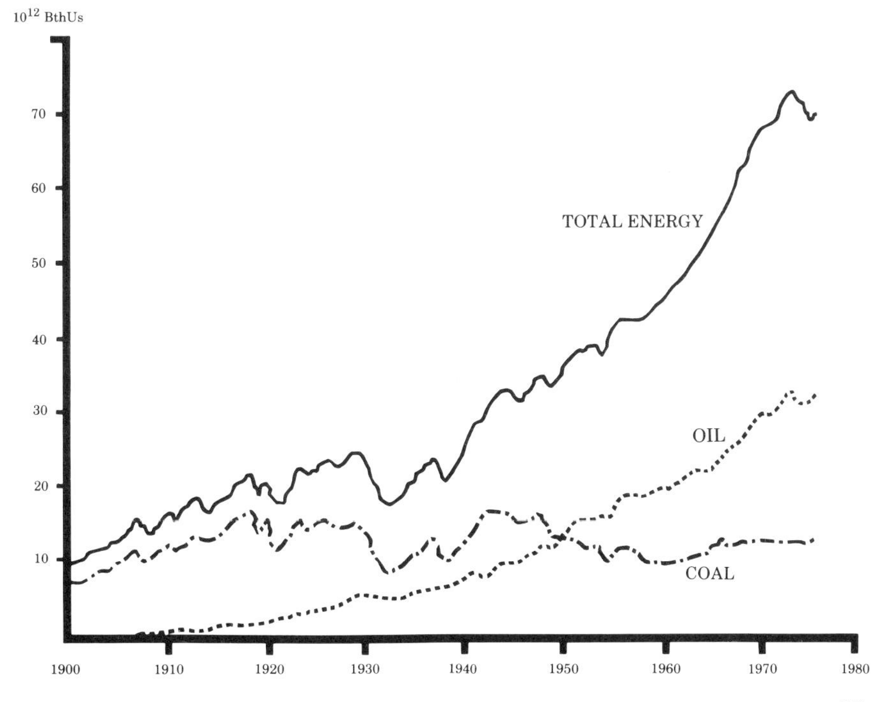

West of the Rockies, Californian production had only one economic alternative until the seven year construction of the Panama Canal was completed in 1914. That was to ship to the Far East. However, alternative energy supplies to oil, particularly coal, were very limited and local demand managed to absorb nearly all the oil produced until 1923. In that year, new fields opened up virtually overnight in the Los Angeles area. Californian production suddenly doubled to around 36m tons per year and seaborne shipments had to start in a big way.

Oil exports to the Far East began to build up, with US companies establishing refining and distribution outlets in Japan. Nevertheless, this export trade was very much secondary to the intercoastal trade immediately set up from the Pacific to the Atlantic shores of the US via the Panama Canal. In 1923, nearly 8 million tons, or 20% of Californian output, was shipped to the East Coast. Nearly all of these movements were crude oil and, due to the lack of tankers, had to be shipped in cases – the non-bulk sector of the oil shipping scene was not dead yet.

Refined products were rapidly substituted for crude shipments as West Coast refiners expanded their plants to cover the newfound local output. In 1923, these inter-US coastal shipments alone represented 15% of world deepsea oil trades. This explosion in Californian production was not to be repeated and with stagnant output and growing local demand, excess for Panama shipment gradually declined. By 1927, this trade had halved to 4m tons per year and during the 1930s tailed off to an insignificant 1-2m tons per year.

Unlike the sharp but short impact of Californian oil on the world shipping scene, the new production areas east of the Rockies had a growing influence, not only on world seaborne trades, but on the whole attitude of the oil industry towards tankers. The first of these areas to become a significant producer was the Gulf Coast. In 1901, Spindletop was struck, near Beaumont in southern Texas, only 20 miles from Port Arthur on the Sabine Lake, itself less than 20 miles from the Gulf of Mexico. Following this famous "gusher", other oil fields were quickly developed all along the coast of Texas and Louisiana.

Spindletop began the most fantastic oil rush. In four years the output of the Gulf was more than that of the old Appalachian fields in the north east. Local demand could not absorb this volume of output and excesses had to be shipped to East Coast markets from Gulf Ports, such as Port Arthur, Sabine, Baton Rouge, New Orleans and Galveston.

By 1906, Mid-Continent fields directly north of Spindletop had overtaken the Gulf Coast output. Many of the companies involved in the early Gulf strikes were also participating in these inland areas; in particular two companies, which were later to become two of the largest in the world, the Gulf Refining Company of Texas (established in 1901, soon to develop into Gulf Oil Corporation) and the Texas Fuel Company (also established in 1901 and later called the Texas Company, then simply Texaco).

Both had been forced to move north as their coastal production began to drop.

Due to such companies, there was a natural tendency to pipe new oil finds south to the refineries and oil ports already established to serve Gulf Coast oil. However, other Mid-Continent producers, notably the Standard and those tied to its empire, preferred to connect their inland fields into the existing north-east pipeline networks, centred on the old Appalachian fields, to the East Coast markets.

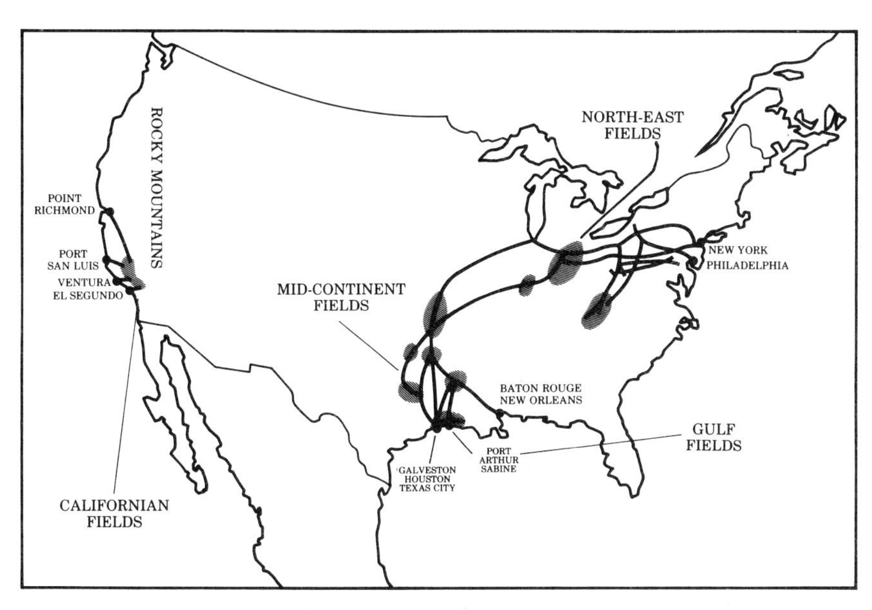

USA OILFIELDS, PIPELINES AND OIL PORTS—c. 1920

These rival methods of transporting Mid-Continent production to the East-Coast quickly became established. The one to the south by 400/500 miles of crude oil pipeline and then some 2,000 miles by sea round to the East Coast. The other, also to the East Coast, via over 1,500 miles of crude oil pipelines. The major difference between these two routes, apart from their length and modes of transportation, was in their ownership. The southern route was independent of the grip of the Standard. The state of Texas made sure that the power of Rockefeller within its boundaries never became too great. But the northern route was effectively owned 100% by the Standard through its stranglehold over interstate pipelines. Just as Samuel's cheap bulk tanker routes to the Far East via Suez had allowed Shell to become established against the might of the Standard in the 1890s, so another major supply route was available to the Standard's competitors giving them the opportunity to bypass the monopoly on domestic distribution which the Standard had so carefully built up over the years.

The key to the survival of these independent southern oil companies was their ability to supply the East Coast competitively by tanker from Gulf ports. The alternative would have been to export and, since the Standard or other growing organisations such as the Royal Dutch Shell Group, controlled foreign markets, amalgamations or takeovers would have been inevitable. In any case, export markets were not necessarily large enough for them, and the only market big enough and growing fast enough to allow them entry without being squeezed out by the tight grip of established companies was the US East Coast – and it was the cheapness of tankers, which allowed them to succeed.

The southern route turned out to be not only cheaper than the northern route, even though it was nearly twice as long, but also far more capable of rapid expansion to meet the booming Mid-Continent output. Helped by the post-First World War surplus of vessels, the southern route by 1920 was openly acknowledged as being at least 10% cheaper than the northern. More and more Mid-Continent crude was piped to the growing Gulf ports and shipped around to the East Coast. When the Great Depression of the 1930s caused the tanker market to collapse completely, there could be no further argument about which route was better. Even the Standard had been forced to recognise this and had, in fact, started to switch to the southern route, to remain competitive, as early as 1909.

Tankers had shown to the US oil industry, and hence the rest of the world, that they were unbeatable over long distances. For companies such as Gulf and Texas, they had captured significant East Coast and, later, foreign markets, and allowed them to retain control over major volumes of Mid-Continent and Gulf production, without becoming subservient to the Standard. Unlike the situation in the Far East with Samuel, tankers had actually taken away trade from the overland route rather than an alternative sea route. By so doing, they had increased world tanker demand by a huge amount – some 20% – so large were the volumes which could have been moved to the East Coast by pipelines. Tankers were no longer a separate part of the oil scene simply representing sea transportation. They were now an integral and competing part of the world oil transportation scene.

The search for oil did not stop in Texas but continued south throughout almost all of Central and South America. In most areas finds were limited and used as substitutes for imports of US oil, tending to reduce the demand for tankers. But in two areas, production soon became far more than local markets could absorb, again forcing companies to export excess and, again, considerably add to tanker demand. These areas were Mexico and Venezuela.

Mexican oil was first struck in 1901 by two California oil men, Doheny and Canfield, 53 miles west of Tampico on the Mexian east coast. However, being very heavy, this crude was of no use as a source of illuminating oil and lacked both suitable and local export markets. It was only in 1904, when the output of similar heavy grades of US Gulf crudes started to falter, that Mexican oil found a ready market as a replacement. The Mexican oil boom was on. By 1911,

Mexico had become the world's third largest producer at 2.0 million tons per year compared with 29.7m tons per year from the US and 9.1m tons per year from Russia. By 1921, with the decline of Russian output following the Revolution, and significant growth in Mexican output, it became second only to the US.

By far the largest market for Mexican exports was the US East Coast. During the 1910s around 50% went to the US, by the early 1920s 60 to 70%. The rest went mostly to Western Europe; the Old World still retained some influence in the Caribbean for it had not yet become a "US pond". Europe had managed to get a stake of oil for itself here. Mexico rapidly became very important for both oil and tankers, but this was not to last. Growing political friction and overproduction of her natural resources by foreign oil companies caused output to decline dramatically in the mid-1920s. The situtation continued to deteriorate and by 1928 exports were only 4.6m tons per year compared with their peak of 25.2m tons per year in 1922. There was no improvement and in 1938, with output crippled, the Mexican Government expropriated foreign oil properties. To complete the picture, oil companies banded together to boycott Mexico and exports dried up completely.

GULF OF MEXICO AND CARIBBEAN OILFIELDS AND PORTS—c.1980

If it had not been for the incredibly fast development of Venezuelan exports during the 1920s, at the exact time that Mexican shipments were plummeting downward, the repercussions of the collapse of the Mexican oil industry on the world tanker market would have been disastrous. In 1922, tanker movements from Mexico accounted for 62% of world deepsea trade of oil. Potentially well over half the world's tankers would have had to have been laid up or scrapped by 1928 with the downfall of Mexico.

For both the oil and tanker industries, the advent of Venezuelan output was ideal. What could have been better for tankers than the replacement of Mexican shipments by larger export volumes from a Gulf neighbour? Imagine the problems if the only new source of supply had been, say, in the Far East. Companies involved in the old Mexican industry would not have been involved in the new. Fleets of tankers would have had to be sold off to be bought for the new trades, and, with new voyages and new oceans to be crossed, completely different types and sizes of tankers would probably have been needed. Old fleets would have had to be scrapped to be replaced by new designs. Venezuela allowed the existing oil and tanker worlds to shift away quietly from Mexico with the minimum of disruption, and if it had not been for the Venezuelan availability, today's tanker industry would very probably be quite different from what we know today.

Commercial oil was first struck in Venezuela in 1914 by Royal Dutch/Shell, in the Lake Maracaibo area, in the north-west. In the 1920s, in the same part of the country, the large American companies also found oil. By 1927, Venezuela had become the second largest oil exporter in the world, by 1928 the second largest producer, and by 1929, at 19.2m tons per year, the largest exporter – a position it kept until the 1950s.

In 1928, exports from the US peaked, and less and less domestic production could be spared for export. As a result of growing demand for oil outside the Western Hemisphere, the traditional importers of US oil had to look more to Venezuela. The US still found it economic to import Venezuelan oil into the East Coast and to export from the Gulf Coast, but gradually from the mid-1920s to the Second World War, the proportion of Venezuelan oil which was exported to the US declined from some 50% to 30% as more went to the rest of the world.

For nearly the whole of these 40 years, the US and the Caribbean dominated both the oil and tanker scenes. Compared with the old 19th century trades, East Coast ports such as New York and Philadelphia had had to turn from loading to discharge facilities. The new oil loading ports of the US were now along the Gulf Coast. From these came a completely new oil trade, the huge inter-US coastal movements for the old East Coast ports. From the Caribbean loading ports, oil flowed to both the East Coast and the rest of the world.

The pattern of oil transportation with the Western Hemisphere had become very complex, particularly within the US itself. By the Second World War, America led the world in oil and pipeline technology and had caught up

Western Europe, if not overtaken her, in tanker construction and operation. The massive inter-Western Hemisphere deepsea oil trades became the backbone of tanker demand, but were very much part and parcel of the American, not the international, oil and tanker scenes. The rest of the world had its own sizeable trades from this same loading area, over longer distances to foreign markets, such as Western Europe and Japan, but even in these America took an interest with the ever presence of its multinational oil companies.

During these years, around 50% of world tanker loadings were for the inter-Western Hemisphere trades. For instance, in 1925 inter-US Coastal trades amounted to 16.7 million tons per year and by 1935, 37.8m tons, while exports from the Caribbean to the US totalled 11m tons per year in 1925, but had fallen to 7.8m tons in 1935. It was no wonder that the US Gulf and, later during this period, the Caribbean, became the centre of the tanker charter market – not only for the US but also for the rest of the world. Additional oil could always be purchased here and charters found for idle tonnage.

The focal point of the tanker world had definitely shifted across the Atlantic and even south from the big 19th century oil ports of New York and Philadelphia. By the Second World War, it had moved away from the US, across the waters of the Caribbean towards South America.

10 RESTRUCTURING THE MARKET

Just as the 1880s had been the right time, for a variety of different reasons, for the deepsea tanker to be born, 40 years later the time had come for a major restructuring of the tanker market. Again it was not just one factor which caused this, but a number of seemingly unrelated events, most of which had started some 10 years earlier in the 1910s. By 1920, only a small force was necessary to push the market away from the virtual monopoly of ownership by oil companies, which it had enjoyed for around half a century. This was the beginning of the "independent sector" of the market, where tankers were owned by pure shipowners with no involvement in oil, so creating one of the most (if not *the* most) competitive free international markets in the world.

During the 19th century, tank ships and tankers had taken up only a small part of the base load of oil movements on the high seas, leaving the rest to package shipments in general cargo sailing ships. Any sudden changes in oil shipping demand had also been taken up by these package shipments, not by the bulk vessels. As regular package shipments were phased out in the new century, it was now left to the tanker to handle both the long term base demand plus any short term fluctuations. Admittedly if demand suddenly shot up, with the lack of spare bulk capacity, package shipments had to be used and sent on general cargo steam ships. In 1923 and '24, the proportion of Standard Oil's*

*Standard Oil of New Jersey – see page 64.

total shipments in cases went up to 30% from less than 5% for the earlier years of 1919 to 1922, setting back to around 10% for the subsequent years of 1925 to 1927. This was principally due to the explosion of Californian shipments. But if demand suddenly dropped, it was now the tanker which had to go into lay-up, rather than the general cargo sailing ship, which had to look for other goods to carry.

The tide had turned against the sailing ship in the 1880s with the introduction of steel hulls and the triple-expansion steam engine. By the 1910's, it was only a few fanatical diehards who were still building deepsea sailing ships. As steam became more and more competitive, sail was forced into less and less rewarding trades. For instance, the Standard's British subsidiary, the Anglo-American Oil Company, started to sell off its sailing ships in 1911. In the First World War, what was left of the world's sailing fleet was decimated; sunk or damaged beyond repair. During the last days of sail, it was the big and beautiful clippers dashing back and forth between Europe and Australia in the last of the grain races, at average speeds topping 8½ knots, that captured the limelight. But illuminating oil was still an essential cargo for this dying breed, particularly from the US to South America, South Africa and Australasia, where bulk oil had yet to become the norm: the route was south from New York to Brazil, then across to Cape Town and catching the trade winds to the Far East.

Following the war, oil companies no longer had the option to use sailing ships for deepsea package shipments. This is not to say that there were no sailing ships used at all in oil trades, but only in coastal, lake or river trades. The general cargo steamship was available, but expensive. However throughout the 1920s, 20% of US exports were package not bulk, but by the Second World War these, too, had completely died out.

In 1920 there was no independent sector of the tanker market worth speaking of. The new US Gulf Coast oil companies had all followed the secure practice before the war of owning their oil barges and tankers to ensure maintenance of a guaranteed supply of oil to their customers in the face of the power of the Standard. When the Baku was nationalised and the First World War played havoc with any balance between tanker supply and demand, it was only oil companies which felt the brunt of these disruptions to their tanker operations. By 1920, oil companies were not so keen to own 100% of their tanker requirements. Far better, some said, for there to be an independent tanker–owning sector to take the risk of any sudden downturn in demand, as had been the case with the independently-owned sailing ships used for package shipments before the war.

One of the main reasons why such a comment could be given credence at this time was that the continual fight for existence, against the stranglehold which the Standard had tried to maintain over supply routes, was over. If the Standard had still been in existence in the 1920s, it might have been a very different story. But the trend was set. The power of the Standard had become

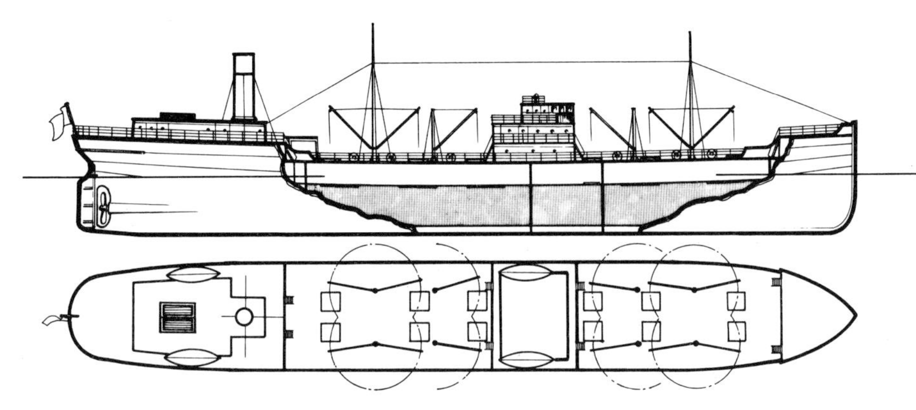

Case oil 'tween decker. Early 20th century.

too great and by the 1900s America was out to tumble Rockefeller and his empire. By 1910, the Standard had 80% of the US market and over 60% of Western Europe's – nearer 75% in Britain. But in 1911 Rockefeller's enemies tasted success. US anti-trust legislation broke the Standard up into 34 separate individual companies. The oil "Octopus" no longer gripped and controlled world oil and seaborne trade.

The initial reactions of the various parts of the Rockefeller empire was stunned inactivity. They just did not know how to operate on their own. Gradually they learned and from the remnants of the great "Octopus" rose three new giants: Standard Oil of New Jersey (the original parent organisation of the Standard, later known as Esso and, now, as Exxon), Standard Oil of California (known as Socal or Chevron) and Socony Mobil Oil Company (or just Mobil). However, there was now no single guiding hand over this empire and the break-up of the Standard was a major turning point in both the oil and tanker industries. Both were now freer and hence more competitive. New elements could survive without being throttled in their infancies, and existing companies could stop for ever looking over their shoulders to see who was going to be stabbed in the back, and when.

Added to this new freedom, the oil industry was becoming far more complex. As well as new companies creating new markets in new parts of the world, the large international oil groups often operated like a number of separate small companies. Until the First World War, individual foreign affiliates of large oil companies were given almost complete autonomy over their operations. In some instances, tankers were chartered "in" by one affiliate, while an affiliate of the same group had surpluses which it chartered "out" on the open market rather than exchanging with its brother organisation. This lack of overall control by parents of international companies, which lasted throughout this inter-war period, left the oil industry even more fragmented than it appeared from the outside.

With the continuous expansion there was constant pressure on finances. The internal fragmentation of the industry inevitably meant that surpluses of cash were not readily redistributed to needy areas. Support services such as tankers did not always come top of the investment list. Not only small, but also parts of large, oil companies were constantly on the look out for organisations prepared to finance tankers for them.

By the end of the First World War, the mood of oil companies had moved very surely away from tanker fleet ownership. The immediate post war surplus of tonnage and the inevitable fall in rates from the wartime dizzy heights only helped to emphasise the need for change. The demand for an independent sector existed, even the price was there, with oil companies willing to pay for flexibility and freedom from the worry of possible lay ups to their own vessels. All that was lacking was the supply, the independent owner prepared to risk the investment. After the war the last pieces of the jig-saw came suddenly into place. The Norwegians arrived on the scene.

Norwegians were always seafarers, as far back as can be remembered. High mountains, narrow valleys and a multitude of small islands forced them to rely on water as a major means of communication. Unlike her rich European neighbours, Norway had never developed into sophisticated passenger and cargo liner services, but had remained in bulk shipping. For centuries, she had specialised in the Swedish timber trade to England. The trade went back to the 16th century when Britain had started to run out of cheap wood, been forced to import it, and had turned to coal for energy. In the 19th century with the era of free trade following the removal of European flag restrictions, the Norwegians moved into many other types of bulk cargo – iron ore, grain and coal itself.

With a plentiful supply of cheap oak and pine, Norwegian owners were reluctant to move into metal-hulled shipping and into steamships. Low value bulk cargoes did not, in any case, warrant expensive shipping. Wooden shipbuilding was the mainstay of many small coastal Norwegian towns. Right up to the First World War, the Norwegian shipping industry remained centred on the wooden sailing ship. By the time the war did come, many Norwegian owners were being gradually squeezed out of their traditional trades by new steamships. Freight rates for their sailing ships had been getting worse and worse, leaving them with little or no foreign exchange. As Norwegian yards had not developed into metal-hulled steam ship construction for the same reasons of lack of cash, the Norwegian owners had to look abroad for both new and second-hand steam tonnage. But with no foreign money, they could not afford the competitive new vessels so badly needed.

The war was a godsend to the Norwegian shipping industry. Even though most of their fleet was lost during it – and what was left damaged and virtually useless – high wartime freight rates, and more than adequate insurance claims, agreeably compensated owners.

At the end of the war, the Norwegians had lots of ready cash. Some of the wartime profit was forced into newbuildings, the Norwegian government making tax exemptions for new vessels on insurance losses. Otherwise second-hand tonnage was bought, principally from Britain. From being a nation of sailing ship owners, almost overnight they became steam ship men.

Within the post-war replacement programme, some tankers were inevitably bought. Oil was a bulk cargo and so a province of the Norwegians. It was, however, not until the mid-1920s that the real development began. By this time, the Norwegians had become aware of the needs of the oil industry, but found that their purchases of second-hand British war tonnage had been a bad move. This old steam shipping was inefficient and expensive to run. What was needed was new tonnage, but the post-war surplus of cash had now disappeared. Now came the last small push which sent the Norwegians into tankers in a big way – a recurring theme throughout the history of shipping – ready credit.

TANKER CHARTER RATES

Medium-rates for dirty tankers fixed to U.K. Cont. with loading one up to two months after fixture.

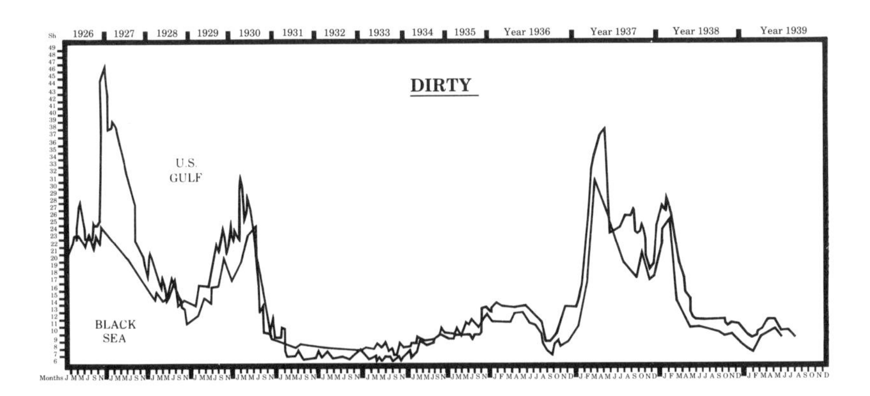

Source: Conrad Boe Ltd. A/S, Oslo

Even if the Norwegians had run out of cash by the 1920s, the rest of Europe and America certainly had not. Although by no means as good as the fantastic rates of the war, tanker rates from 1923 to 1930 were more than acceptable, and banks were only too willing to lend foreign money at highly advantageous rates to the Norwegians. Owners found that they could order without any down payment. Often the first payment of 25% did not have to be made until the vessel was delivered, and the remainder covered by deferred credit. By negotiating five or 10 year time charters with oil companies, the whole back to back finance could be arranged during, if not before, the start of construction. Under this scheme small Norwegian owners could afford to build brand new tankers with virtually no cash involvement themselves.

In the 12 years from 1920 to 1932, the Norwegian fleet jumped from 0.2m DWT to 2.3m DWT or from 3% to 18% of the world tanker fleet – the major growth coming in the years between 1927 and 1932. One of the first and foremost Norwegian tanker owners was Wilh Wilhelmsen, who by 1923, owned some 40% of Norwegian tanker tonnage. Wilhelmsen had moved into tankers in 1913 with some 100 years of ship owning behind him. Many Norwegian whaling owners moved into tankers as a natural redirection during the 1920s and 30s when the whaling catch was very much on the decline. One such famous owner to follow this route was Earling Naess in the early 1930s.

So the independent sector came into being. Backed by guaranteed oil company charters, a huge fleet of new vessels was built, just in time for the Great Depression of the 1930s. As the world went into its worst economic slump, international trade withered away. All types and sizes of shipping were affected, including tankers. From 1931 to 1936, tanker rates were terrible and with too many tankers, some had to be laid up. By 1933, 15% of the world's fleet was in lay up, principally American and British vessels. However, this was just the time when the initial guarantee charters of the Norwegian vessels were running out and so the number of Norwegian tankers in lay up soon rose to surpass that of the US and to nearly equal the total of British lay ups. By the mid-30s, 0.4m DWT or 15% of the Norwegian tanker fleet was also idle.

As the Norwegian vessels went into lay up, so the oil companies could take their tonnage out of lay up, and the sight of Norwegian, rather than their own, vessels being idle convinced them that they were absolutely right in fostering independent tanker owners. There was now no turning back from their gradual retreat from tanker ownership. It was felt best that the oil companies should continue to own some tankers; to keep up with technology of the industry and to ensure that, in good markets, they could not be held completely to ransom by the independents. But there was certainly no need for them to own nearly 100% of world tankers and, by the Second World War, the independent sector had grown to account for 39% of world tanker tonnage and a permanent part of the tanker scene.

Free international market forces may have created a large independent sector, but there were other forces also operating within the tanker market, which were not so free and had just as much, if not more, influence during this period on ownership. While Europe had been shedding most of her restrictive maritime laws during the middle years of the 19th century, the US had been strengthening hers. By the 20th century, only US-built and owned tonnage could be used from one US port to another, as is still the case today. The massive inter-US coastal oil trades which built up during the early part of the 20th century were, therefore, never available to the open market. These oil cabotage movements were completely protected by the US for the US, so guaranteeing employment to their own shipyards in building tankers, their own shipowners in operating tankers, and to US merchant seamen in manning tankers.

Ownership of the World Tanker Fleet

	1900	*1923*	*1938*
Oil companies	} 90%	59%	54%
Governments		16%	7%
Independents	10%	25%	39%
	100%	100%	100%

This protective US coastal legislation was not new – it went back all the way to the end of the American War of Independence in the late 18th century. The first Congress of the new Confederation had set about protecting coastwise and inland water trade for US tonnage through a series of preferential tariffs. In 1817, the law of cabotage was further strengthened when a new Act was introduced allowing goods, not in US-owned vessels, carried between two US ports, to be "forfeited". Although US coasting legislation was now firmly established, the gradual expansion of the US and the addition of new territories continually led to anomalies in coastal trading. During the 19th century, various amendments and further maritime Acts were introduced in an attempt to correct these, but it was not until 1920 when the definitive legislation was passed – the famous or infamous "Jones Act".

Senator Wesley Jones was the Chairman of the Senate Commerce Committee, established to draft the new all embracing merchant marine act. To put it mildly, he was pro-American. He openly admitted that as Americans ". . . we must look after ours. We are entering no brotherly love Sunday School picnic in seeking our part in the world's carrying trade. Fair means and foul will be used to defeat us . . .". The Americans were convinced that most of Europe was still upholding flag protection in practice, even if it had repealed the greater part of such legislation a century earlier. Why should the United States of America not do likewise? In any case, as Senator Jones put it, "We, the United States, should really lead the world's shipping, whereas the US ranks second to

England". There was the additional argument that domestic trades had to be maintained for the US maritime industry so it could "serve as a naval or military auxiliary in time of war or national emergency", plus the growing problem of what to do with the post World War I surplus of US flag tankers. So the Jones Act was passed in 1920. At the same time the US Shipping Board had to work out how best to dispose of the now unwanted massive surplus of wartime built merchant vessels – not just tankers – to the best interests of the nation.

The Jones Act was somewhat irrelevant where tankers were concerned. The big inter-coastal oil trades of the 20th Century had been firmly reserved for US-built owned and registered tonnage by legislation going back over a century. For other types of tonnage, the Act tied up loopholes such as the timber trade from Washington State on the West Coast to the East Coast, which was being moved overland to Vancouver in Canada in order to escape having to be shipped in US flag tonnage. This was now stopped. Perhaps more important, the Jones Act signified the growing isolationism of the US from the rest of the world. Apart from during the Second World War, the US tanker industry became more and more orientated to domestic, or, at least, Western Hemisphere trades. The gradual decline of oil exports from US ports only helped to emphasise this trend and it was not until the 1970s that the US was, very unpleasantly, jolted to look outside the protective shell which she had built up around her during the inter-war years.

One of the main reasons why the Jones Act had to be introduced was that US shipping was simply uncompetitive on the open market. Without the protection of such laws, it is highly probable that no US flag tankers would have been used on the US coasts after the First World War. Even before the war, the operating costs of US ships were significantly higher than those abroad. US flag tankers could not compete with Europe flag vessels and by the Second World War, they were around 25% more expensive. High wages also affected US shipbuilding, but excellent productivity in US yards allowed them to remain competitive with European prices beyond the First World War.

A continual argument put up for these monopolistic regulations was, and still is, that of "national security"; to ensure that, in times of crisis, the American people still have a vital maritime industry and a tanker fleet capable of serving the nation. Whether reasonable or not, the US tax payer has certainly had to pay for the privilege. US oil companies have had to employ high cost tonnage and ensure that they had a minimum of 10% extra US flag carrying capacity to cover any operational contingencies on US coastal trades. These extra costs have been passed straight on to the US oil consumer. But, on the other hand, US shipyards have had guaranteed domestic demand against which to plan and invest. Even if Western Europe, at the time, saw the Jones Act as a potential threat against the freedom of the high seas, when the Second World War came the Allies, and particularly Britain, were only too glad to call upon the strength of the US shipyards, especially for tankers.

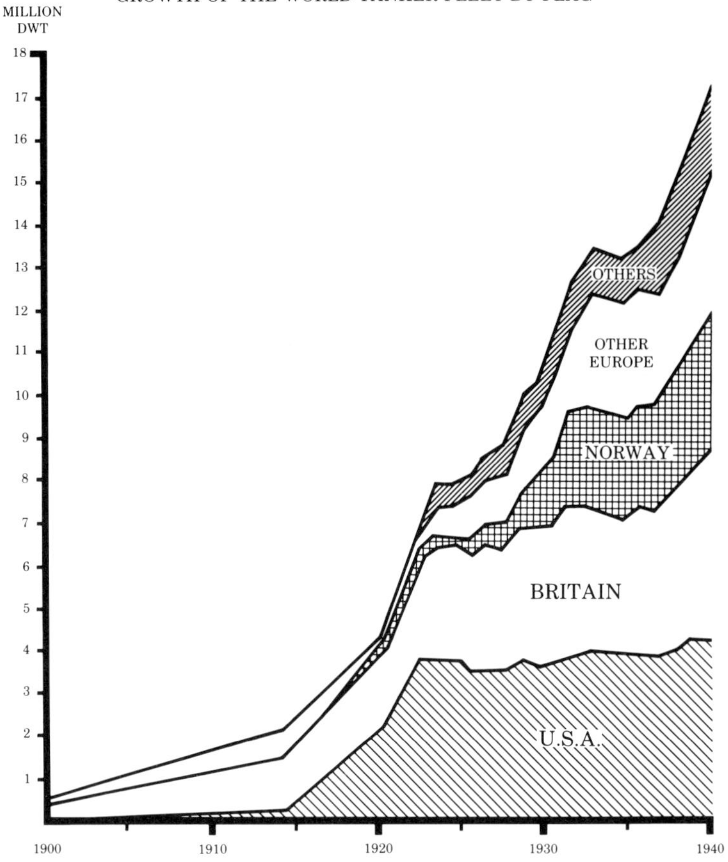

Note 1) GRC converted to DWT by factor of 1.5
2) No official figures for 1901 to 1913 and 1915 to 1919 inclusive

It is perhaps ironic that it was not these cabotage laws which were the real spur to US tanker construction during the first half of the century, but the two World Wars themselves. It was the ship operators not the shipyards which gained most out of the Jones Act. The protected coastal tanker trades gave an underlying steady demand for US tankers during the period, but new orders under the US flag were nearly all for replacements to old oil company tonnage, rather than new vessels to cover new demand.

Up to the First World War, US tanker demand and construction grew with the new trades from the US Gulf to the East Coast, but even by 1914 only 11% of world tankage tonnage was under US flag. The war caused the picture to change completely. There were simply not enough tankers around to supply

Europe, principally Britain, with the oil needed for the war. Old cargo vessels were converted and liners had their ballast tankers and double bottoms requisitioned for oil. 1.8 million tons of oil were carried by these methods from July 3rd, 1917, when they were introduced, to November, 1918. But still there was not enough capacity. In 1916, the Germans embarked on the mass slaughter of Atlantic, and even US flag tonnage with some 200 submarines, and, in 1917, convoys had to be introduced. These slowed down the fleet and added at least another 10% to the already soaring tanker demand. US yards, therefore, entered into a massive tanker construction programme. Much of this tonnage went under US flag and was built for the US Government so that it that it could directly help the allied cause. By 1922, with all vessels under this programme delivered, the US flag covered 50% of world tanker tonnage!

The Shipping Act of 1916 gave the US Shipping Board the authority to acquire merchant tonnage and, on the 6th April, 1917, the US Emergency Fleet Corporation was established for just this purpose. The Corporation sponsored a massive marine programme, not only ordering new vessels, but also expanding existing yards and developing new ones. By the 1st August, 1919, the Corporation had contracted for, or requisitioned from private shipowners, 119 new tankers, totalling 1.1m DWT, of which 52 had already been delivered. To indicate how large this programme was, the world tanker fleet in 1919 was only 536 vessels, totalling 3.9m DWT. In these two and a half years total deliveries by US yards were some 80 tankers.

It was not just the Corporation which was ordering tankers from US yards to replace war losses. From 1916 to 1921, US yards delivered 316 tankers, totalling 3.2m DWT, but once Western European yards were free of war orders, in the early 1920s, owners looked again towards Europe, not America, for tanker tonnage. In 1914, Britain still dominated world shipbuilding. She had a far superior steel industry, and US yards had yet to catch up with much of British shipbuilding technology. In 1917, 73 out of 235 US slipways were still for wooden ship construction. It was Britain that was developing the huge, fast Atlantic passenger liners; Britain that was in the forefront of steam and steel construction; and Britain that was well ahead of the US in tanker hull design. After the American Civil War, at the end of the 19th century, the US had lost interest in building ships for foreign owners, and so, by 1917, 75% of US ship construction was for the Navy. The First World War and the Shipping Board changed the whole US maritime construction scheme, revitalising it and setting it on the road to compete with, and eventually beat, its European counterparts, but this was not to happen until just before the Second World War.

Unfortunately for the US, the huge fleet owned by the Emergency Fleet Corporation was of little use after the war, and only 29 vessels or 0.3m DWT of it had been suspended or cancelled by the Corporation at the end of the war. As tanker demand settled down to normal levels again in the early 1920s, a considerable surplus of US flag tonnage quickly developed. The US Shipping

Board had little success in selling these surplus Government tankers, as they were not as suitable for international trading as excess British-built vessels and certainly the Norwegians did not want them. By November 1st, 1921, the Board had a total of 89 tankers or 0.8m DWT on its hands. As it could not operate them, it had to lay them up. In 1923 out of some 3.8m DWT of US flag tankers, only 2.1m DWT was trading in domestic trades, 0.9m DWT had been forced into less rewarding foreign trades, and some 0.8m DWT was still idle. It was not until the Second World War that the US tanker industry got its house in order and this surplus was mopped up. Then the same thing was to happen again – another huge burst of US tanker construction and, at the end of the war, another massive surplus.

In 1900, Western Europe flags had controlled over 90% of world tanker tonnage and Britain alone, 60%. Although only a small fleet, by today's standards, of 0.6m DWT, this virtual monopoly over tanker registration was a direct reflection of the Old World's past power and dominance over world shipbuilding and ownership of modern tonnage. Past, but not future. The growth of US coastal oil trades was just one example of the changing world where Europe no longer controlled the sea. Oil trades were now under the power of the US either directly through cabotage laws or indirectly thorugh import and export trades to and from her shores. By the 1920s, therefore, Europe was left with well under 50% of world tanker demand in which to put her vessels and Britain with considerably less, especially with the surplus of US flag tonnage.

Out of what was left of the tanker world to the Europeans, there were major shifts in registration and ownership compared with the situation before the war. The German registry, which had been the second largest in the world, after the British, was effectively destroyed. With the defeat of Germany, all German flag tankers were seized and transferred, principally to the US flag (90% having been owned by the German subsidiary of Esso) but also to the British flag. Some German tankers escaped this by being switched to Danzig registration, as under the Treaty of Versailles in 1920 they were immune from seizures, and later, in 1935, transferred to Panamanian flag.

Other shifts within European control were, of course, due to the rise of the Norwegian fleet. The war, therefore, caused a decline in European oil company-owned tonnage, while the post war period saw a rise in independently-owned vessels. These events were completely outside the control of the British. So, not only was Europe's share of the world tanker market declining before its eyes, Britain's share of what was left was being reduced at the same time. By 1923, the world tanker fleet had grown to 7.7m DWT or 13 times its size in 1900; by 1939 to 16.6m DWT or nearly 30 times. But, by 1923 the US flag controlled 48% of the world fleet, Western Europe 45% and Britain only 33% compared to the 60% she could boast in 1900. By 1939, with the rise of the independent sector, the balance had been redressed somewhat, with the US flag at 25% and Western Europe at 62%, but Britain was now down to 26%. The

MAJOR WORLD SEABORNE OIL MOVEMENTS – 1925

(Total 55 million tons per year)

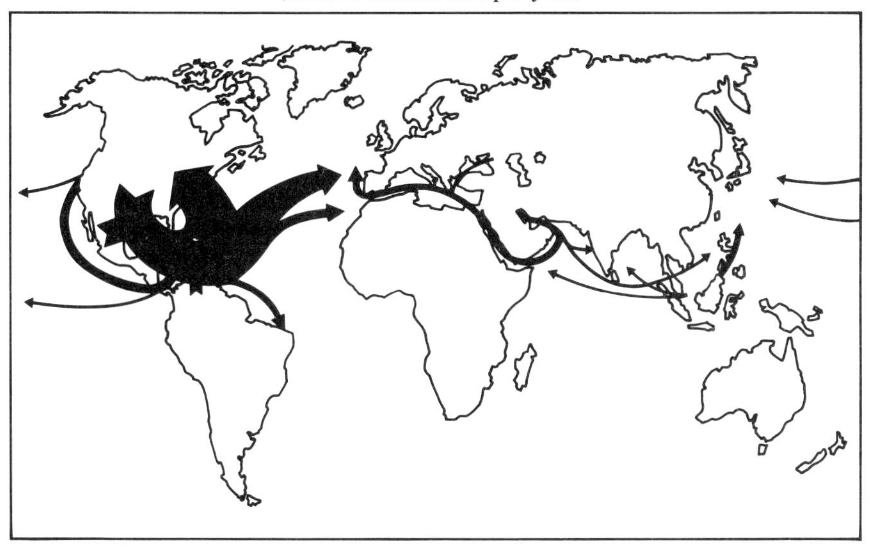

MAJOR WORLD TANKER TRADES – 1925

(Total 5.4 million DWT)

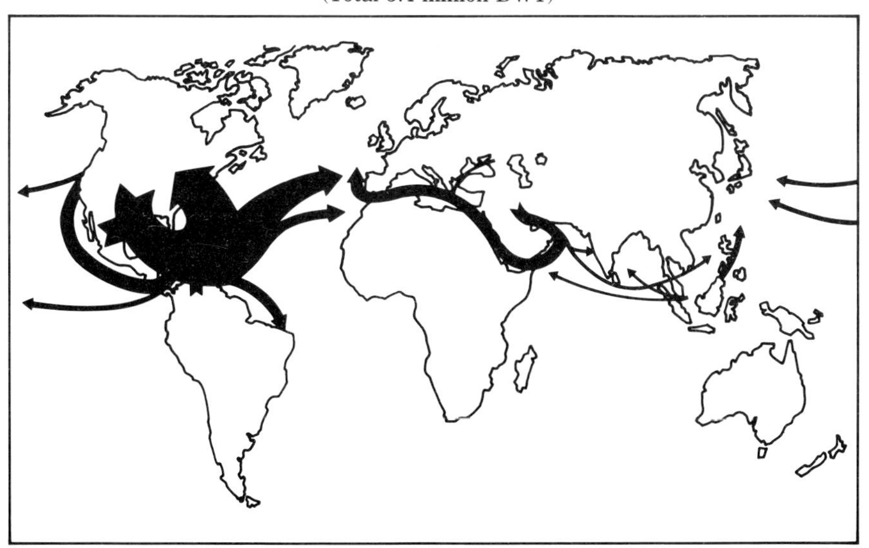

US had arrived on the tanker market and Britain no longer ruled supreme.

Although ownership had become more diffuse, both in type of owner and registration, the tanker market was still one which could be manipulated. There was not control to the degree which the Standard had had prior to 1911, but there was still enough, in certain hands, for it to be far from a true example of free competition. The market itself had changed from inter-oil company exchanges to an open market where independently owned tonnage was chartered by oil companies. In 1900, the Standard and Shell alone had owned, or had on charter, 62% of world tanker tonnage, but by 1938, Shell, which had become the largest single tanker owner, owned only 10% of the world fleet, followed, now, by Esso.

The observed market place was in the old bourses – the Baltic in London had been and still was the largest chartering market for tanker tonnage. Other tanker charter markets had grown up, and, except for New York which handled a considerable volume of Gulf and Caribbean fixtures, these were basically for local coastal trades. However when the Great Depression of the '30s brought six terrible years for the market (1931-1936), owners managed to join together in cooperative action to push rates up and so move the market place out of the bourses into their own hands.

This slump in rates was in neither the oil companies' nor the independents' interests. Both sectors owned vessels and neither could obtain reasonable returns on investment. For the oil companies, there was the additional, if not more potent, disadvantage of low spot tanker rates reflected in oil prices, depressing a signficant proportion of the oil market as well as the tanker market.

In 1934, a tanker pooling arrangement was established, known as the Schierwater Plan. By raising a levy on the employed tankers of owners in the scheme, laid-up tonnage of the same owners was given a subsidy, thus inducing tankers into lay-up. It was a relative success. Rates on the route US Gulf/UK Cont went up from 8s. 6d a ton to 12s. 6d a ton, or nearly 50%. With oil companies controlling around 55% of supply, and the independents being predominantly under one flag (Norway), it was possible to "rig" the market, but only to this limited degree. In the days of Rockefeller, his rule of thumb was a minimum control of 75% before any market was his. By the 1930s, such a high percentage control by any one group was virtually impossible. The fact that there was some success for Schierwater, even though it was only limited, was and indication that the tanker market had yet to become the freest market in the world.

11 NEW CARGOES . . . NEW PROBLEMS

The rise and fall of new and old production areas may have dictated the broad trend in tanker trades, but the nature of these trades was also changing as different types of oil cargoes had to be shipped across the seas. With new cargoes, the trading patterns of tankers became more complex and new requirements were placed on the designers, builders and operators of these now highly specialised vessels.

In the 19th century, the oil supply pattern had been very simple. As the oil market was still very unsophisticated, and refining processes very basic, significant proportions of the crude oil input to refineries were either unwanted or wasted. It did not, therefore, make good economic sense to move crude oil (and hence these unsaleable fractions) around. Far better to locate refineries as near the oil fields as possible. From the refineries, products were distributed to either local or far off markets. Local distribution was no problem, it could be done by horse and cart, or even on foot. To get the products to more distant overland markets either inland waterways and barges could be used, or the growing network of railways. Overseas markets could only be covered by shipping the oil on the high seas.

When the crude oil pipeline was developed, a new set of rules came into play. It was now cheaper to move crude oil overland even with the unwanted costs, than just the refined products (the first US pipeline for clean, light products was not built until 1918). Refineries could now be moved away from the oil fields and sited at the most economic location – as long as the terrain between them and the oil fields was not too mountainous. But it was still not economic to place them overseas.

At the turn of the century, American oil was being piped some 300 miles to be refined on the Atlantic coast, where there was a large natural market and good seaports for foreign shipments. Russian oil was piped less than 10 miles and refined on the Caspian. It was impractical to pipe it over the long distances to the markets of Europe for refining. In the Far East, refineries were established at the nearest coastline to the oil fields, which themselves were normally on or very near the sea. The major exception to this pattern was the French market where the Government, by imposing its high differential import tariff on refined products, had forced crude oil rather than products to be imported and refined domestically, principally American crude oil.

The American and French refining industries were "market" located whereas the Russian and Far East, were "source" located. During the first half of the 20th century, there was nothing new to change radically the economies of siting refineries. Since most new finds were well away from the large local markets, the Mid-West and the Gulf in the US, Mexico and Venezuela in the Caribbean and Persia in the Middle East, refineries all tended to be "source" located during this period, the exception being in California and certain American hinterland areas east of the Rockies, where there were local markets large enough to absorb production.

A few small refineries were built in Europe, in addition to the French, but it was principally refined products, not crude oil, which were shipped across the Atlantic during this period. It was in the Western Hemisphere where crude shipments became important. To begin with, the existing crude pipeline networks from the Mid-Continent to the East Coast fed the old refineries on this coast with any shortfalls of crude. However, as the tanker route from the Gulf ports became more competitive than the pipeline route, supplies were switched to the sea. East Coast refining capacity was expanded from 12m to 32m tons per year from 1918 to 1938, most of this additional capacity having to be fed by tanker supplies of crude since the old Appalachian fields could not be expanded. By 1938, 24.3m tons per year of crude oil were being shipped into the East Coast, 3.6m tons from Mexico and Venezuela, 0.1m for California and 20.6m from the US Gulf Coast.

In addition to these crude oil shipments to US refineries, significant quantities of crude oil were also shipped in from both Mexico and the Gulf Coast for direct burning, as a fuel oil substitute. The first finds of both Mexican and Gulf crudes were very much heavier than the old North-East crudes and, as in Russia and the Far East, immediately created their own fuel oil markets – the railways in Mexico and the cotton plantations in the Southern states. By leaving these crudes in the open air for a few days, the volatile fractions escaped, effectively creating fuel oil.

From 1900 to 1910, the US fuel oil market jumped from under 2m tons per year to over 15m tons per year, of which around 8m tons was unrefined crude oil. The big markets on the East Coast turned to fuel oil – smelters, cement and brick plants, factories and even homes. Railways and ships started to turn to fuel oil, although coal fought against any loss of these markets. By the late 1910s, coal still had the East Coast railways, but oil had captured the locomotive market west of the Rockies and in the Mid-Continent. Fuel oil was far easier to turn on and off and so for many heavy industries and domestic users it was preferred to coal. At the peak of Mexican production in the early 1920s, some 80% of crude output was being shipped directly to the US, principally as a fuel oil substitute. It would be wrong, however, to give the impression that the US switched completely from coal to oil. This was by no means the case. Even by 1938, coal accounted for 54% of the total US energy market and was cheaper than oil – the average yearly price of US coal at the mine head ranged from $1.14 to $4.20 per ton between 1900 and 1938, whereas the average yearly price of crude at the well was between $4.45 and $22.40 per ton.

Another crude oil sea trade developed in the Western Hemisphere during this period. By no means as important for tankers as these others, it was still interesting. In Venezuela, the waters at the mouth of Lake Maracaibo were very shallow and not dredged for large tankers until after the Second World War. Initially, therefore, refineries had to be located outside the Maracaibo bars, since there was very little local demand and virtually all of the output of any refineries had to be exported by sea. Added to this, Shell had little desire to build a plant in Venezuela itself, partly because of the geographical difficulities of laying down a long pipeline to a good coastal loading point, and partly because of the political climate in Venezuela. In 1917, it took an unusual compromise step by building a refinery on the nearby Dutch island Curacao, some 50 miles off the Venezuelan mainland and just over 200 miles away from the bars. Gulf, on the other hand, set up a transhipment terminal on the Venezuelan coast in the mid 1920s, outside the bars at Las Piedras to feed its US refineries. In 1931, Esso acquired a similar export plant to Shell's on the neighbouring and slightly nearer island of Aruba, also part of the Lesser Antilles chain.

To feed these deepwater terminals with crude oil, a fleet of specially shallow draught tankers was built up. These vessels, nicknamed "Mosquitoes", were around 3,000 DWT with a 13 foot draught, and shuttled back and forth between the terminals in Lake Maricaibo and the deepwater facilities, often in convoys, to catch the high water on the bars.

In was 1901 when the first of the "source"-located Gulf refineries, at Port Arthur, came on stream. Others followed soon after, at Baton Rouge, Texas City, Houston and Beaumont. In Mexico plants were built at Tampico and, for the aforementioned Venezuelan crude, off the coast of Curacao and Aruba. Shipments from these new plants were, in part, in competition with the old trades from the US East Coast plants. However, it soon became apparent that output from these old plants should be reserved for the local East Coast markets. Export trades switched to the Gulf and Caribbean refineries, thus cutting out the two-legged journey of crude oil to the East Coast and then products to foreign markets. By the late 1920s, the East Coast plants were effectively reserved for supplying the local market and US exports came from the now huge Gulf Coast refineries. By 1928, Texas alone had more refining capacity, 33m tons per year, than the whole of the East Coast states put together. By 1938, the Gulf states of Texas and Louisiana had a total of 70m tons per year refining capacity (Mississippi had none at this time) or 36% of the total in the USA.

It was not just the location of crude oil production and refining which was to affect tanker demand during this period. What was just as, if not more, important was the changing market for oil itself. To the traditional main line oil products of kerosine and fuel oil were added two others, gas oil and gasoline, plus a host of minor products creating literally hundreds of different grades of oil, with each importing country and climatic zone requiring its own special specification. It was in refined products that the real complexities of shipping arose.

As early as 1806, gas had been used for street lighting. The first gas main in a public street was in London, between the Haymarket and St James Street, the gas being extracted from coal. The same principle had reached the US by 1817, when gas street lighting was introduced in Baltimore. For the rest of the century, gas lighting grew in popularity and in competition with kerosine. In the US, both coal and natural gas were used as sources, but, by the turn of the century, a light residue cut from crude oil or "gas oil" was also being used.

By the 20th century, there was another and far more serious competitor than gas to illuminating oil. Electric lighting was catching on. To start with it was only the big cities of Europe and America which could afford this luxury, but gradually electricity spread out into towns and rural areas. The demand for kerosine began to fall. Sales peaked in Europe in 1905 and in the States in 1910. From representing 50% of sales in 1900, kerosine, the most important oil product of the 19th century, fell to some 10% of sales by the advent of the Second World War.

Undoubtedly the biggest revolution in the oil market, in more ways than one, was the invention of the internal combustion engine. Dr. N. A. Otto had first designed an engine which could run on a light cut of petroleum in 1876, but it was too large and too heavy for road vehicles. It was not until 1885 that another German, Karl Benz, developed a smaller model and demonstrated it on the road a year later. The automobile fuelled by "benzine" or gasoline had arrived.

At first, the automobile was for the well-off or the eccentric in Europe and America alone, and a limited export volume of gasoline from the US started up in the late 19th century. But Henry Ford changed all that. In 1908 he started mass production of his "Model T" touring car priced at under $400.

Ford had created the four-wheeled contraption that *anyone* could afford. Anyone, that is, who was lucky enough to live in a rich country. In the early 20th century, this meant Europe and the US, plus a few isolated European colonies. But Europe, in her futile blood bath of the First World War, destroyed much of her wealth and had to wait until after the Second World War to enjoy fully such mass luxury.

It was America which was to experience the huge boom in domestic car ownership during the 1910s and '20s. The resulting peak in gasoline sales was fantastic. In 1900 there were 8,000 cars registered in America and less than 100 trucks; by 1910 there were 458,000 cars and 10,000 trucks and, by 1920, 8,132,000 cars and 1,108,000 trucks. From fewer than 1m tons per annum in 1900, gasoline sales were up to 11m by 1920 and 58m in 1938. Geared towards kerosine production, the US oil industry was forced to reorientate completely. In 1938, gasoline represented 48% of US oil consumption and even by 1930, 30% of sales.

As well as the gasoline engine, the Diesel engine appeared early in the century. Dr. Rudolf Diesel patented this alternative internal combustion engine in 1892 – ideally to run on almost any type of fuel. However, he decided to concentrate on liquid petroluem as its fuel after his experimental model blew up on powdered coal. Gas oil (known later as diesel oil) or fuel oil was found to be the best, and soon the diesel engine was in use on both land and sea using these heavier cuts of oil.

By 1920, the oil market had diversified tremendously. As well as the four main line products of gasoline, kerosine, gas oil and fuel oil, there was the ever-growing host of minor products for use as solvents, lubricating oils, cutting oils, ointments, roofing and road materials and so on. The tanker now had various roles to play in getting oil from "well-to-wick". It had to supply some refineries with crude oil from the production areas, it had to distribute all the output of certain refineries to the consuming areas and, for other refineries, it had to carry away those products which could not be sold locally.

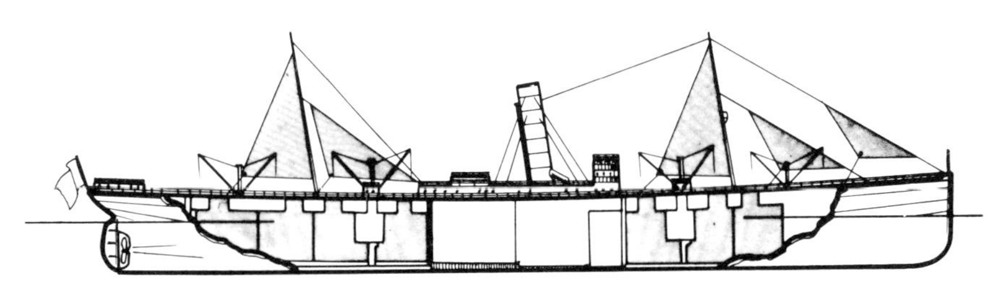

"Narragansett" 1903. 13 knots, triple expansion—built for Anglo-American by Scott's Shipbuilding & Engineering Co. for Atlantic trade.

The type of cargoes could vary tremendously from very heavy crudes or fuel oils with specific gravities of 0.96 to light gasoline cuts with specific gravities of 0.73. Light cargoes needed perhaps 30% more space than heavy for the same weight of oil to be shipped. The heavy grades often needed to be heated to ensure ease of pumping in and out. On some routes, it was desirable to carry more than one grade of oil at the same time, but to ensure no cross contamination each had to be segregated. Since crudes and fuel oils are black, and gas oils, kerosines and gasolines white, great care had to be taken to clean a tanker switched from dirty to clean (or black to white).

Each oil company had its own individual oil trades and different requirements for its tankers. From the Caribbean to the US East Coast, cargoes were primarily crude and fuel oil, but to Europe they covered the whole range of products. From the US Gulf Coast to the East Coast roughly equal quantities of crude and products were being moved by the 1930s, but, of the products, over half was gasoline. Not only did different trades mean different cargoes, but also different bunker requirements. Each voyage, therefore, had an optimum design of tanker which had just the right cargo space and just the right bunker capacity. Surpluses and deficits of particular products would occur, and a tanker could find that having discharged a cargo of, say, gas oil, it had to reload gasoline at the same port to be shipped out to where it had loaded the gas oil. But two such loaded leg voyages were very much the exception. Tankers generally did not have to clean after each trip and carried paying cargo on only one of their voyage legs.

12 DESIGNING FACTORS

Although there was a tremendous growth in the size of the tanker fleet during this period – from 0.6m DWT in 1900 to 16.1m DWT in 1938 – and in total number of tankers – from 182 to 1,731 – neither the average nor even the largest size of tanker saw anything like the same order of change. In 1900, the average size of tank ship was 3,500 DWT (including sailing ships and barges designed for oil), while the largest tankers being built were just under 6,000 DWT. By 1938, the average size had risen to only 9,300 DWT and the largest to around 22,000 DWT. In fact it had been as early as 1903 that the first 12,500 tonner had been built, at Scott's at Greenock, Britain. This was the *Narragansett* built for the British subsidiary of the Standard, the Anglo-American Oil Co., the world's largest tanker for a number of years.

As an indication of how far the US construction industry was behind the European yards, it was not until 1914 that 11,000 DWT was achieved, with two vessels for Standard Oil of New Jersey at the Newport News yard. On the other side of the Atlantic, British yards had moved up to 16,000 DWT with a series of 10, the first of which was delivered in 1913 for the shipping company of Mexican Eagle. However by 1921, American yards could claim the largest world tanker when Esso ordered two 22,600 DWT vessels, the *William Rockefeller* and the *J. D. Achbold*, also from Newport News. But only a handful of tankers of this size were built until after the Second World War, most being no more than 15,000 DWT.

With tanker demand increased nearly 30 times, why did ship size increase so little? There *were* technical limitations in pushing size up too quickly and restrictions in construction capacity, but certainly not such that prevented tankers larger than 15,000 DWT or even 22,000 DWT being generally built by the Second World War.

Huge passenger liners had been built since the turn of the century to race across the Atlantic of speeds of 25 knots or more – two to three times the speed of the tanker. For instance, in 1907 two liners of this speed, the *Mauretania* and the *Lusitania* were built in Britain for the Cunard Steam Ship Company. They were both around 32,000 GRT and as large as a modern 70,000 DWT tanker. As early as 1858, the 19,000 GRT *Great Eastern* passenger liner was launched, admittedly somewhat of a freak for her time. The reason for the relatively slow increase in size was not to be found in inadequate construction facilities. As far as speed was concerned, a low value, non-perishable commodity like oil simply could not afford the luxury of huge power units and high bunker consumption.

The answer to the mystery lies in the tanker voyages themselves. In 1900, the main deepsea tanker trades were across the Atlantic, 3,400 nautical miles each way. The shift of US exports from the East to the Gulf Coast increased this voyage to 4,800 miles, although from the Caribbean it was slightly shorter at 4,200 miles. But it was not on these trades that the biggest change occured, but on the US Gulf and Caribbean to the US East Coast routes. These voyages were only 1,700 miles each way, half the length of the old Atlantic voyages. For the tanker trades to Europe, there was, therefore, little change in voyage length, but, for the new massive US coastal trades, voyages were shorter than the old 19th century deepsea trades.

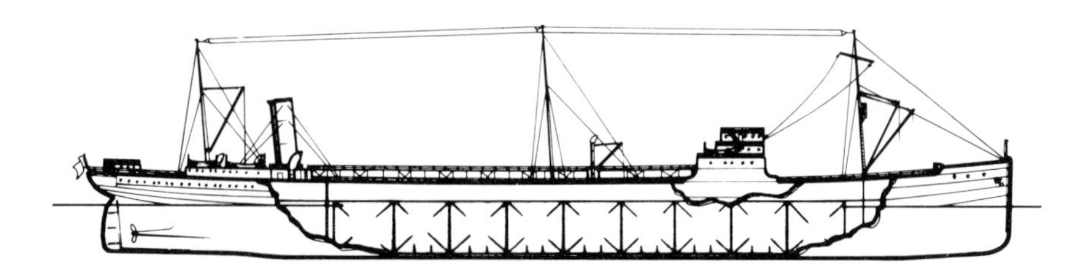

U.S. built 20,000 DWT, LOA 527'. Three decks—shelter deck and general cargo derricks. For U.S. Coastal trade.

With shorter voyages, tankers on average spent more time in port and less time at sea. Larger vessels cut the costs of shipping oil at sea, but in port they often meant higher costs. Deeper channels had to be dredged, and larger storage systems built at both loading and discharge terminals to accommodate both the bigger vessel and their larger cargoes. The longer the voyage, the easier it was for the economies of scale at sea to pay off the diseconomies at port; the shorter the voyage, the converse. Consequently it was the changing pattern of oil trades to shorter voyages that gave little economic incentive to increase the vessel size as rapidly as was technically possible.

Admittedly, this argument applied far more to the domestic US tanker industry than the European, since most of these shorter voyages were US cabotage trades and hence reserved for US flag tonnage. However, the loading ports of the US Gulf and Caribbean were very much biased to serving the US East Coast and not Europe, so, what was good enough for America, had to be good enough for the rest of the world. Furthermore the US yards, which became very important in world tanker terms during and after the Great War for both US and non-US owners, were naturally geared to building for these domestic trades. Voyage and port restrictions both contributed to dampening down any desire to build the world's largest tankers.

In addition, a further factor which possibly had more impact on tanker size was the sub-division of the oil market into the many more products which had to be shipped. From just the one main line grade of illuminating oil in the 19th century, before fuel oil was carried, there were now four, plus all the minor grades and their further divisions into different specifications for different parts of the world. This variety of grades was particularly obvious in Western Europe where each country developed a different set of quality restrictions for each grade. It was very rare for the same grade of oil to be suitable for more than one country at one time. Assuming that tanker demand on the main routes was now split into four rather than one single grade, tankers still could not carry four different grades of oil at the same time. So even though trade across the Atlantic increased 17-fold between 1900 and 1938, from 2m to 37m tons per year, for the tanker it effectively increased only four-fold where one grade was carried, or eight-fold if two were carried. It did not, therefore, follow simply that because overall demand was increased the size of vessels should increase too!

But it would be untrue to say that there were *no* technical problems in building larger tankers. There were many, though none which need have seriously impaired the size developed by the Second World War. At the turn of the century, the tanker was little more than a standard merchant ship which had had its cargo holds compartmentalised and filled with oil. In fact, owners initially thought that a homogeneous cargo like oil would be safer to carry than the normal non-homogeneous general cargo, which was usually loaded haphazardly into the holds with little regard for weight distribution. A shipping correspondent in 1893 said about tankers " . . . we do not proceed on synthetic principles, but we dump cargo of any sort into a ship of any size and wait to see what happens". As a result of this trial and error method of developing tankers, there had been many tragic losses. To begin with marine architects did not understand how great the stresses and strains inside a tanker could be. The number of transverse bulkheads were too few and hold sizes thus too large. Ships cracked and broke up under the effects of large volumes of liquid cargoes shifting about in heavy seas. 19th century tankers were also prone to roll excessively causing great strains to the hull. Riveting was inadequate. Tankers came apart at the seams. So, by the 20th century, designers and builders were naturally proceeding very cautiously in developing tanker size.

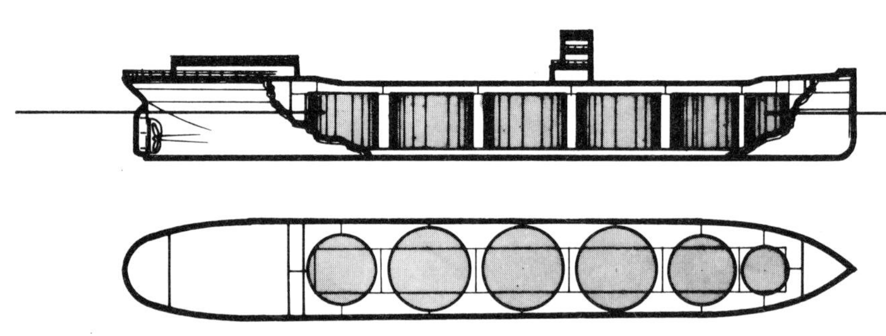

Cylindrical tanker, built during World War I.

By 1900, steel had virtually replaced wood in new ship construction. This is not to say that wooden tank sailers were not built after 1900 or that existing sailing vessels not converted to deepsea tank ships, but only five tank sailers were created in 1900, three in 1902, three in 1903. After that none were built for the high seas, only for coastal and inland water trades. Steam-driven cargo ships were also converted to tank ships, partly due to the continuing fear in some owners' minds over the real safety of the tanker, partly due to the cheapness of buying old cargo ships and converting them, but mainly as a method of creating oil carrying vessels quickly.

Vertical cylindrical tankers were favoured, especially during the First World War when there was a great upsurge in tanker demand. This shape of oil tank could be easily fitted onto the existing double bottoms of cargo ships, inside the holds. Sometimes six large cylindrical tanks would be fitted, at other times twice as many would be crammed into the hull. However, these vessels were highly uneconomic in terms of carrying capacity, only 9,000 tons of oil could be shipped in a 12,000-tonner. Tankers were even designed as two, long, side-by-side cylindrical tanks, but these were only small vessels for short sea trades or specialised cargoes like lubricating oils.

Cylindrical tankers were not the norm and did not last beyond the Great War. Neither did concrete tankers. Again built as a wartime contingency, these needed much less steel than normal tankers. The hull was made of thin concrete walls reinforced with a very high percentage of steel bars and although an excellent method for smaller sizes, concrete was little used for deep-sea vessels. Only a handful of 7,500 DWT tankers were built by this method – for the US Emergency Fleet Corp – and this was, in fact, the *only* special tanker design created under the massive US war construction programme.

Steel and rivets were the standard materials of the day and apart from these few exceptions, bulk oil carrying vessels were fully fledged tankers, where the cargo was carried next to the steel hull. Unfortunately, rivets and oil were never ideally matched. The rivet, whether steel or iron, suffered from cathodic corrosion and also could work loose. Once rivets began to go in one part of a tanker, they could go right through the entire hull. The dynamic movement of a constantly shifting cargo caused this problem, resulting in continuous changes in stresses and strains on the hull in high seas. Double and even triple riveting had, therefore, to be introduced in those areas known to be prone to excessive strain. Different types and shapes of rivets were tested and tried in an attempt to make tankers "water-tight", on the basis that, if water could not get in, oil could not get out. By the 1920s, the riveting of new tankers had become reasonably satisfactory, but it had also become one of the major, if not the greatest, expense in the construction of tankers.

It was by no means unknown for old tankers to have to have their hulls completely re-riveted at special surveys. It became a fact of life that old tankers leaked like sieves. "Never sail beyond the sight of land" was common, if cynical, advice. No wonder that the Americans on the East Coast were to become some of the most highly environmental conscious people in the world after years of battered, old, leaking tankers trudging up and down the coast to and from the Gulf and the Caribbean, only a few miles off shore. Politicians and the media say that tankers are dirty nowadays, but compared to some of the vessels around at this time, modern tankers are clean enough to have a bath in!

The development of the tanker size would probably have been even slower had not a major design breakthrough been made in Britain early in the century. Sir Joseph Isherwood patented a revolutionary new hull frame in 1906. This went a long way towards eliminating the leakage problems which had dogged the traditional "ribbed shell" pattern of tanker hulls. Isherwood did away with the framework of ribs extending upwards from a strong centre keel. In its place, he conceived a design with a number of strong, vertical longitudinal plates or "frames", running the length of the ship and supported by a limited number of heavy vertical transverse frames. The tanker thereby

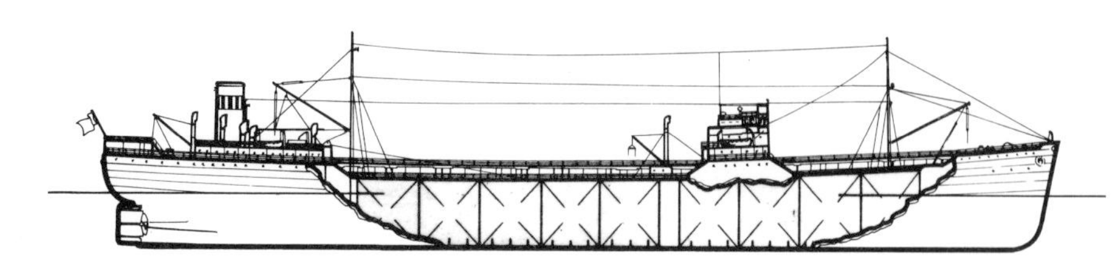

"Scheherezade" 1935. 18,500 DWT, 14 knots. First large French built Isherwood bracketless system. Owners compagnie Auxiliaire de Navigation for Atlantic trade.

changed from being a weak shell into which oil was poured, to a strong lattice work of girders surrounded by a skin of metal filled with oil. The first longitudinal framed tanker was built in 1908, the *Paul Paix*, 6,600 DWT, by Messrs R. Craggs and Sons, England.

The main advantage of the longitudinal system was the increase in longitudinal strength. The weight of steel for a given size of tanker could, therefore, be significantly decreased and the safe size limited lifted from 10 to 15,000 DWT. Isherwood modified his design in 1925 to the "bracketless" longitudinal system, allowing size to be increased beyond 20,000 DWT. The first vessel to be built on this design was the 13,000 DWT *British Inventor* in 1926. Although this design did not reduce vessel weight, it significantly eased construction and maintenance problems. In 1926, a further modification was introduced by combining the transverse and longitudinal framings. This reduced hull weight and opened the way for even larger tankers to be built.

Until the Great War, it was Britain which dominated tanker design and construction. When the US decided that it would enter into a massive war programme, it could not compete with the British know-how and had to rely principally on the old transverse framed cargo ship designs for most of its tankers. The war allowed the US yards to modernise and compete internationally, but it took some time for the technical developments of Britain to be universally accepted throughout US yards. It was not until 1916, for example that Sun Shipbuilding of Pennsylvania built its first longitudinal framed tanker.

By 1918, 380 tankers totalling some 3.5 million DWT, or over 80% of the total world tanker fleet, had longitudinal framing. It was not only tankers which switched to this type of construction. In the same year 560 cargo and passenger vessels totalling 4.4 million DWT plus 104 lakers, barges, dredgers and trawlers totalling some 0.3 million DWT were also built on the Isherwood system. However, the huge surge of tonnage built during, and immediately after, the war set this trend back and in 1924, six years later, while 573 tankers totalling 5.5 million DWT were Isherwood-designed, longitudinal framing encompassed only 71% of the total world fleet.

An added bonus to the Isherwood design was that it strengthened the tanker sufficiently to relocate the engine room aft, a design heralded by the *Gluckauf* and used for a few years until the size of tankers increased to the point where the ribbed shell was not safe unless the engine room was placed amid-ship. Reverting to the aft location meant that the old problems of leakage into the tail shaft tunnel from the stern cargo tanks was solved. However, the bridge and officers accommodation was retained amid-ships creating the "three island design with poop, bridge and forecastle, while the engineers' and deck crew's accommodation remained aft.

Machinery aft meant that trimming was easier, although longitudinal sagging was still a problem with the fixed weight of the machinery at one end having to be counterbalanced by the variable weight of either cargo or ballast water at the other. Cargo tanks were now all together and only one pump room was needed where two might have had to be built before, one on either side of the machinery space. The two cargo sections, fore and aft, in the old tankers, had had to be completely separate for everything but fuel oil cargoes, since any interconnecting pipeline between pump rooms had to pass through the engine and boiler space. Leakage from this line would have been disastrous for grades lighter thus more volatile than fuel oil. Such inflexibility was not a problem so early in the century, but would soon have become one with the variety of different grades increasing all the time.

With more than one grade of oil now being shipped, there were obvious advantages in designing flexible tankers which could carry more than one grade at a time. Theoretically, most tankers could have carried more than one grade, assuming that they had more than one pump and a pipeline system which allowed separate tanks to be filled and emptied independently. In practice, it was not as simple as this. A very limited cross-contamination between different grades of oil was permissible. In general light grades could contaminate heavy, but not vice versa, as heavy grades were lower quality. In any case, dirty grades could not mix with clean grades since customers would refuse the soiled white products. Leakage of bulkheads was far too common for shippers to be able to put two different cargoes in adjacent tanks and expect no cross-contamination. To ensure complete "segregation" as opposed to just "separation", a cofferdam had to be built between the two tanks.

The early multi-grade tankers did not bother about full segregation. Different grades were separated by a single bulkhead. One example of such a vessel is the 1908 standard class with machinery astern and a pump room in the bow. The eight transverse bulkheads plus the one centre longitudinal bulkhead, created 14 different tanks. One of the four pumps in the pump room was set aside for ballast, one was connected to the four foreward cargo tanks for kerosine, one to the middle six for crude and the last to the aft four for benzine.

A pump room was just as good as a cofferdam to segregate tanks. So with the engine room aft and out of the way and a cofferdam placed at each end of the total tank space for general safety, the pump room could be placed in the middle of the cargo tanks if two grade segregation was required. By building either another pump room, or cofferdam, inside the cargo space, three or more grade segregation could be achieved. In 1917, a coastal tanker for the US Atlantic shores had been designed with five cofferdams and one pump room. Since one cofferdam was between the fire room and the bunker tank, four grade segregation was possible. By the 1920s, four different grades could often be carried on deepsea ships, but only two could normally be segregated. By the Second World War, eight or more grades could be carried but these multi-grade tankers were generally for short sea trades, such as US coastal, rather than across the Atlantic. On these longer, deepsea hauls, it was still the normal practice to use single or two grade ships. The ultimate in this development towards more complex multi-grade tankers was the "General Purpose" tanker, or GP. This could carry both crude and refined products at the same time, was generally around 12,000 DWT and was one of those specialist designs for the integrated oil company who had a range of clean and dirty oils to be regularly shipped on the same trades.

As well as inserting cofferdams and pump rooms in between tanks to ensure no cross-contamination, more sophisticated pipeline and pumping systems had to be developed. If more than one grade of oil was to be carried at the same time, each grade had to have its own pipeline and pump so that it could be not only shipped but also loaded and discharged without contamination.

The increase of grades created not only design problems in handling more than one grade at a time, but also operational problems in switching from one to another between voyages. Cleaning tankers, whether just for trade reasons, or to get the vessel ready for dry dock, was, and still is, not easy. Oil gives off highly explosive and dangerous gases, such as methane, butane and propane. If the proportion of these is high enough in a supposedly empty tank, they can very quickly kill an unsuspecting man.

The old illuminating oils of the 19th century were probably the easiest oil cargoes to carry. They were clean and had little associated gas with them. In the 20th century, the new cargoes created new problems and dangers. Crude oil, for instance, has a lot of sediment, such as sand or earth, still floating around in it, plus rust scale from land tanks and pipelines. Both crude and fuel oil have heavy long chain hydrocarbons or wax in them. These tend to settle out on a long sea journey, so that when the cargo is discharged a coating of sediment and sludge is left clinging to the whole of the inside of the cargo tanks. Black oil tankers soon were found to build up layers of this muck inside them and had to be regularly cleaned out. The inside of the ship's tanks themselves rust, since they alternately carry oil and sea water, and even clean cargoes built up some sediment in the tank bottom. Crude and light products, such as gasoline, have numerous dangerous gases associated with them.

In the 19th century, the standard way of cleaning out a tanker was to fill cargo tanks up with sea water until they overflowed. Any residual oil and gases were thereby forced out. The better owners skimmed off the oil as it rose to the tank tops. Just imagine the rumpus if this practice were reinstated today. This method was fine for illuminating oils, but not for the 20th century cargoes, nor to ensure that the tanks were completely clean. Neither was it very safe to clean a vessel, since oil was left lying all around the ship. No wonder commentators of the time warned that throwing "lighted matches or red hot ashes overboard" could lead to fires.

For many years the only way to clean a tanker properly was to send a squad of men down in to the tanks with buckets, shovels and mops to hand dig the muck out. First the tanks would be filled with steam from the ship's own steam lines for a number of hours. Once this had been blown out of the tanks, the men would go in and hand hose the sides. The solid sediments would be put into buckets and the smaller particles brushed into the suction to be pumped away, the dirty, oily waste being, of course, pumped straight over the side into the sea or harbour. If the vessel was switching from dirty to clean trading, one tank would be completely filled with gas oil or kerosine, as this would dissolve most of the black oil clinging to the tank sides. This would then be pumped from tank to tank to clean each one successively and pumped ashore when finished with for re-refining. Down once again would go the gangs of men to swab the tanks down and dry them off with special cloths. It would take days to carry this out, and was a very expensive operation costing around £7,000 a time. Consequently it was not done too frequently. Cleaning a tanker was dangerous for both the crew and the vessel. A hazard long forgotten was the real possibility of red hot cinders falling from the stack into an open tank top.

If a tanker was dirty, it usually stayed dirty, unless a particular charterer was prepared to pay the cost of cleaning up because he desperately needed a clean ship. The world's tanker fleet, therefore, became split into a "clean" and a "dirty" sector.

A major advance in keeping tankers clean was made when, in the very early 1930s, the Butterworth System of tank cleaning was introduced. Water heated to around 175°F was pumped under very high pressure to a special hose nozzle which could be fitted in any tank top. This nozzle revolved continuously and in such a way that the whole of the inside of the tank was automatically sprayed. The force of water was so great that even rust scale was broken up and could be simply pumped away with the cleaning water. Using this system, dirty tanks still had to be cleaned with gas oil, but rather than having to fill the whole tank up, the gas oil could be pumped through the Butterworth System and recycled, thus dramatically reducing the volume of dirty gas oil created in cleaning the vessel.

TANKER CROSS-SECTION DEVELOPMENTS

1880s

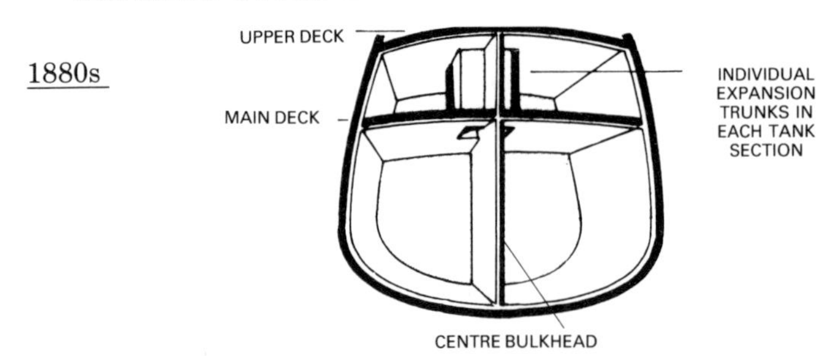

The "Gluckauf" was a typical design for this period. Each oil tank had a separate expansion trunk extending up from the main deck to the upper deck. A centre bulkhead split each tank in to two, creating 12 to 20 individual tanks. Sometimes the expansion trunks would be next to this bulkhead, as is shown, or between this and the hull side walls, or even against the hull. The 'tween deck space was normally used for reserve bunkers or case oil, not bulk oil.

1890s

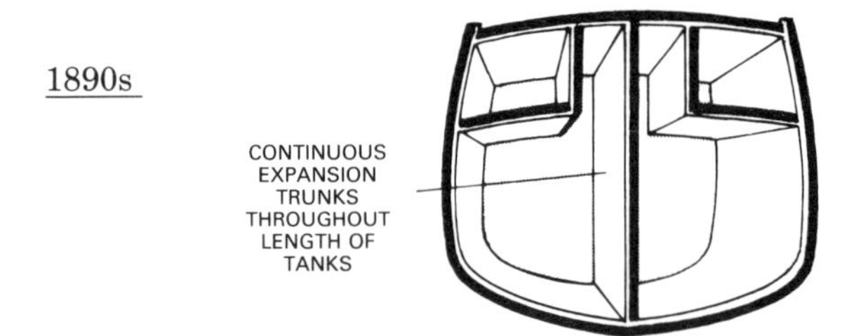

In order to add longitudinal strength, the separate expansion trunks were joined up to form a continuous single trunk throughout the length of the cargo space. Still the space on either side of this trunk was not used for bulk oil, but coal bunkers, and sometimes covered with a wooden not a steel deck.

1900s

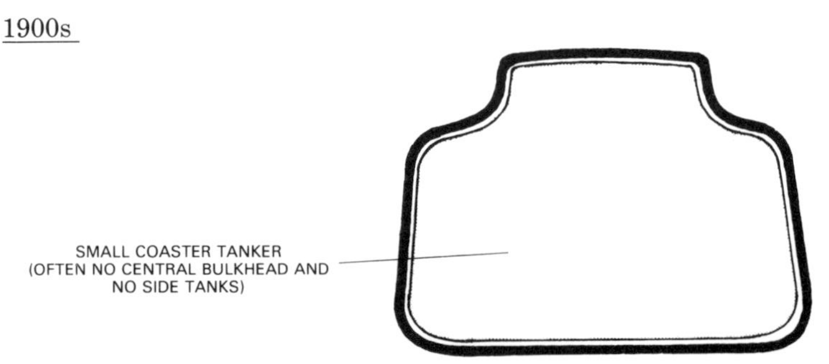

For small coastal tankers, where voyages were short and the waters relatively calm, the spaces on either side of the expansion trunk were dispensed with and the trunk widened out somewhat. These were called trunk or turret tankers and had the added advantage that tonnage dues were reduced with the elimination of the non-paying spaces, either side of the trunk.

For larger vessels, the machinery was moved amid ships, with the result that the poop, bridge and forecastle were separately located on a continuous upper deck. This was the start of the '3 island' era.

TANKER CROSS-SECTION DEVELOPMENTS (continued)

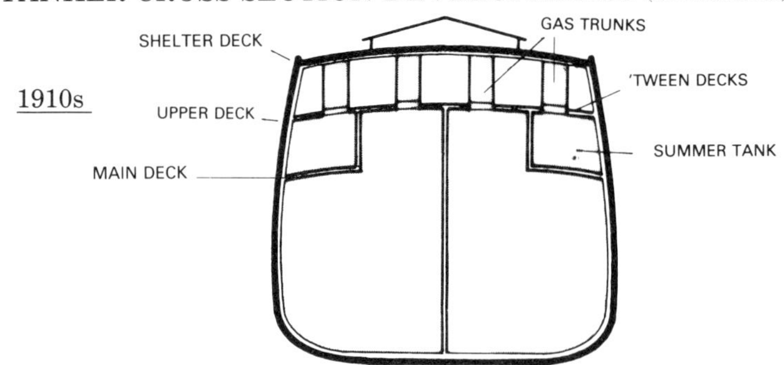

As tankers got even larger, it was found advantageous to add a third deck, the shelter deck, to give extra strength. Although continuous, by having large tonnage openings the shelter deck does not affect the tonnage measurement of the ship, which was still taken from under the upper deck. To begin with the oil hatches were placed on the upper deck and to stop oil gases getting into the 'tween deck space gas trunks extended up to the shelter deck. With more than one grade of oil being carried and engines more efficient and hence using less fuel, the spaces either side of the expansion trunk were used for bulk oil. These spaces were called summer tanks as they allowed addition expansion capacity in hot weather and could also be used for a second grade of oil cargo.

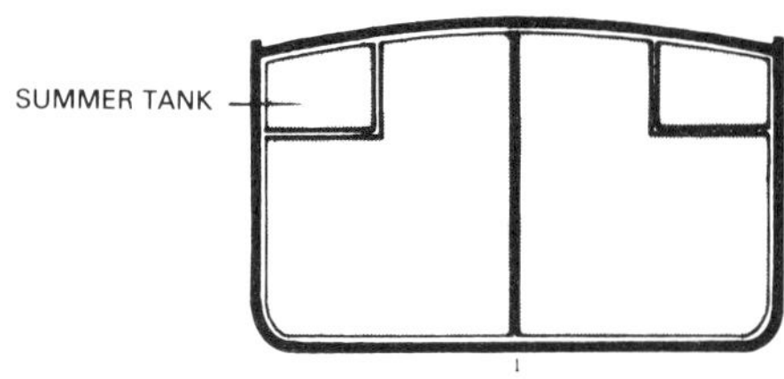

The gas trunks were soon found to be dangerous and were eliminated by extending small trunks up from where the hatches had been to the shelter deck. The oil hatches were now relocated on the shelter deck.

Also at this time certain owners started to dispense with the upper 'tween deck. The development of Isherwood's longitudinal framing helped considerably in this respect. The cross-section of the tanker started to become simpler rather than more complicated. The summer tanks were retained, as was the centre bulkhead.

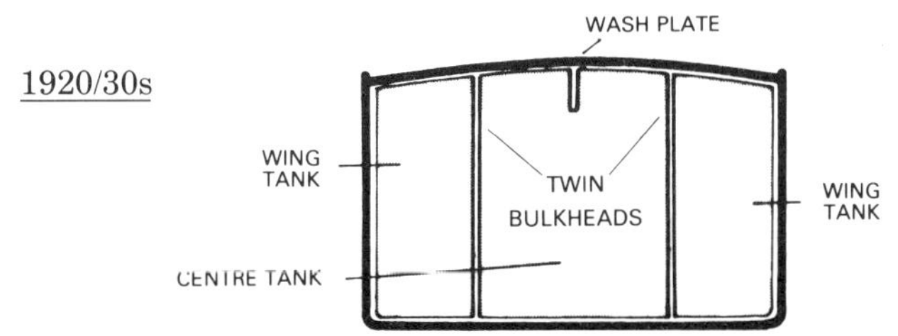

As a further move to increase the longitudinal strength the "twin bulkhead" tanker was introduced and gradually replaced the centre bulkhead design. It gave a direct saving in steel, had fewer areas likely to corrode and was more flexible in loading and trimming. It retained a small central wash plate from the upper deck, ensuring that when full the area of liquid available to move was minimised.

Heavy crude and fuel oils created other problems for the 20th century tanker owners. These very heavy oils were extremely "waxy" and could not be pumped unless heated. Steam heating coils were, therefore, soon installed in the cargo tanks of dirty oil carriers very early in the century to move both Mexican crude and Californian fuel oil. At the other end of the product range, there was gasoline and this possibly caused even more problems. It was soon found that gasoline (plus a limited number of very highly sulphurous crudes) ate away the steel. In the 19th century, the very limited volumes of gasoline shipped in bulk had been found quite useful as a first cargo to a new tank as they aided the 'rusting in' of rivets. However, when steel was used instead of iron, gasoline did not even have this in its favour. Corrosion with gasoline cargoes was so bad that owners often either had to scrap gasoline tankers before they were 10 years old or, if they wished to get the normal 15 years or more service out of them, switch them to dirty trading before they were five years old. Alternatively they could regularly switch between clean and dirty cargoes, but the cleaning operations involved were costly. Nevertheless it was still done on occasions.

Isherwood's longitudinal framing brought more to tanker design than simply strength. It completely changed the internal construction of tankers and made builders re-evaluate many accepted design concepts. One obvious example was the way in which the cross-section of tankers changed. Operators in the 19th century soon learnt, often the hard way, that oil tanks were not to be simple rectangular boxes, certainly not on the heavy seas of the Atlantic. To start with some sort of venting system had to be attached to each tank to get rid of excess gases and also some space had to be left within each tank to allow for expansion and contraction of the oil as the temperature changed. A simple box design created a huge free surface of oil which could slop around in bad weather causing very serious handling and stress problems. When the ship rolled from side to side, the surface of the oil also moved, pulling the centre of gravity of the ship outboards and potentially creating instability.

The answer was simply found in fitting small "expansion" trunks on the top of each tank, significantly reducing the free surface of the cargo plus providing for expansion and contraction.

Until the 1890s, different types, sizes and shapes of expansion trunks were used, some rectangular, some cylindrical. A central bulkhead was used for strength and to split each tank in two, creating 12 to 20 individual tanks per vessel. Sometimes the expansion trunks would be next to this bulkhead, as in the *Gluckauf*, sometimes mid-way between it and the hull sides, and at, other times, actually against the hull itself. The tank top formed the 'main' deck of the ship and the expansion trunks extended up to the "upper" deck.

Around the 1890s, separate expansion trunks were dispensed with and were joined up to form one single continuous central trunk. This added to the longitudinal strength of the vessel, an important consideration as size increased. The space between the two decks which was not used as expansion volume was itself very rarely used for oil during the 19th century, but normally for reserve coal bunkers or even case oil if the ship was to trade on short voyages where bunker capacity was not a problem. The British yard, Swan Hunter, used always to fit these 'tween deck spaces with overhead railways to make it easy to get the reserve bunkers to the boiler room. The deck above these 'tween decks was not necessarily steel or iron, but could be wooden. Above the deck auxiliary sails, in case the tanker ran out of bunkers, and cargo derricks for package cargoes were the norm.

By the turn of the century, the size of tankers had increased enough for a difference in design to be noticeable between small coasters and deep-sea vessels. For some small coasters the spaces on either side of the expansion trunk could be completely dispensed with, if they were not to be used for parcel oil. These vessels did not need reserve bunker capacity and it was better to gain the reduction in tonnage dues by eliminating these closed spaces than keeping them. The expansion trunk was widened somewhat and for the length of the cargo tanks; the top deck of these tankers had a step in it. These vessels were called "trunk" or "turret" tankers.

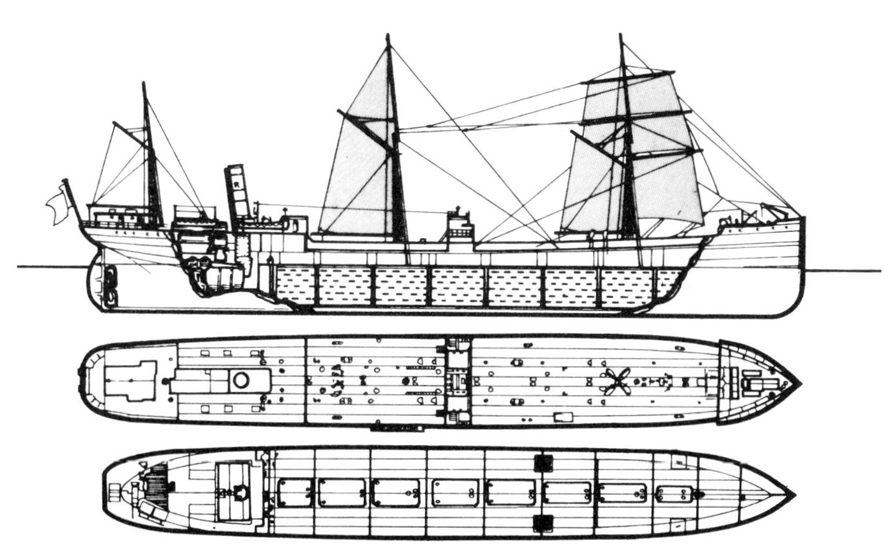

S.S. "Hesperus". Built by Palmers Shipbuilding and Iron Co. Ltd., 1908. dimensions: 428' 0" × 54' 6" × 32' 0" mld. 'Tweendeck–9,600 DWT; 6,400 GRT. Tanker–transverse framed.

With the larger tankers, the machinery was moved amidships for strength. The poop, bridge and forecastle were all built on top of the upper deck and these tankers were known as "well" deck vessels. Auxiliary sails were still retained, although seldom used as bunker consumption and hence the likelihood of running out of fuel reduced with improvements in engine design.

As tankers got even larger in the 1910s, a third deck was incorporated, again to give added longitudinal strength, but also to increase deadweight without a proportional increase of vessel draught. This extra deck was above the upper deck and known as the "shelter" deck. Although a continuous steel deck, the space between the shelter deck and the upper deck was not counted in the assessment of tonnage measurement, and hence the payment of port and canal dues, as long as it had large, permanent tonnage openings in it. To begin with there was little difference between the two and three deck designs. The oil hatches were still in the upper deck, but small gas trunks were extended from the upper to the shelter deck to keep any gases out of the 'tween decks. However, these gas trunks were found to be very dangerous and soon the hatches themselves were located on the shelter deck and the gas trunks turned into connecting oil trunks to the upper deck.

With the increase in engine efficiency there was a general decrease in the demand for large reserves of coal bunkers. The 'tween deck space was available, therefore, for case oil if required and so had large cargo hatches for loading and unloading. Many tankers retained their deck winches and derricks for this purpose. The space between the expansion trunk and the tanker's hull became free for bulk oil cargoes. These wing spaces under the shelter deck became known as "summer" tanks, for in summer seas, vessels were allowed to be loaded to a greater depth: all cargo spaces rather than just the main tanks could then be used. Summer tanks could also be used year round for light oils, such as gasoline. So, just at the time they were needed, "multi-grade" tankers became available with the use of summer tanks. These tanks were sometimes emptied by means of a simple drop valve into the main cargo tanks, but more normally, especially if gasoline was to be carried, by a separate pipe system.

At the same time that the traditional ribbed-shell tanker was being strengthened by a third deck, it was also being replaced by the new longitudinal framing. In this design, no third deck was needed and the cross-section was simplified to a centre bulkhead plus summer tanks. In the 1920s, a further move towards even greater longitudinal strength was made by extending the summer tanks down to become fully fledged "wing" tanks. The centre bulkhead was dispensed with, but a small "wash plate" was left from the upper deck in order to break up the surface area of the oil in the centre tanks. This design required less steel, was stronger and had less horizontal surfaces to keep clean, and so was less prone to corrosion. This basic design was gradually introduced during the 1920s and 1930s giving good operational flexibility in both loading and trimming.

Improved steel technology helped builders pick the best material to give the lightest, strongest and most corrosion resistant ships. However, higher tensile steels were more expensive than the traditional mild steels. An economic balance had to be made between weight savings in using these better materials, and their additional cost. Although the size of tankers may not have shown much change during this period, both the external and internal design had radically altered. This was the period when the modern tanker really came into being. Trial and error had given way to scientific development.

A tanker under construction in Harland and Wolff's Belfast shipyards.

13 THE SURGE OF OIL POWER

Even if size saw only a modest change during this period, the efficiency of the tanker, as a vehicle to carry oil, increased tremendously. Both speed and cargo capacity improved significantly, allowing steaming times to be cut and the volumes of oil shipped per year to be pushed up. Bigger and more powerful pumping systems ensured that the time necessary to load and discharge a full cargo remained roughly constant, at 1½ to 2 days per port, even though cargo sizes increased. Overall voyage times, including time in port, were, therefore, substantially reduced for the tanker fleet as a whole, allowing more voyages to be made each year for each ship.

The big breakthrough in improving carrying power came with the general acceptance of oil as a viable alternative to coal as a fuel for deep-sea vessels. The advantages of oil were considerable. Fuel oil's thermal efficiency was 1.3 times that of coal and so the weight of bunkers which had to be carried on a given voyage could be decreased by some 25%. Oil stowed far better than coal and could be put into places which were totally impractical for coal. It did not have to be man-handled into the boilers, but conveniently piped at the turn of a valve. The space savings were tremendous and all space saved could be redesigned into more oil carrying capacity. Crew numbers and bunkering time could also be significantly reduced and steam got up far more quickly with oil than with coal.

With such advantages, it was perhaps surprising that it took until after the

First World War for oil to become established. Fuel oil had, of course, been available in the 19th century, but neither in sufficient quantities nor in the right locations to compete seriously with coal in the international bunkering business. Baku oil was land-locked until the trans-Caucasian railroad was built in 1883 and, even then, relatively little could be spared for export after the local railway and Caspian steam ship markets had been satisfied. In any case it was very expensive to get Russian fuel oil to the big Northern European ports. Fuel oil at Baku sold at between 1s. 3d and 4s. a ton. Adding the £1 rail cost to Batoum, and the 22s. bulk freight cost to the UK, the delivered price would have been around £2 5s. compared with Welsh coal at 9s. a ton, or five times more. At this price, oil just could not compete against coal, even allowing for all of its advantages. In the Far East, production of the heavy crudes of the Dutch East Indies did not start until the 1890s, leaving little time for output to grow much before the end of the century and in any case this source of fuel oil was a very long way from the major bunker markets in Europe. It was the development of US crudes in the 1900s and particularly Mexican oils in the 1910s which created the major increase in the supply of this new product. However, it still took another 10 to 20 years, until the 1920s, for fuel oil to be accepted.

The reason for the reluctance of shipowners to move from coal to oil was certainly not quality, and not even price. It was guaranteed availability. American fuel oil could be supplied at only three to four times the cost of coal per ton, and since coal-fired machinery consumed three to four times the weight of bunkers per day that an oil-fired unit did, the total cost of fuel was approximately the same. Allowing for the savings in manning and the increases in paying cargo that the oil-fired ship offered, there were definite savings to be made for owners to switch to fuel oil. But coal was everywhere in the world, fuel oil was not. Britain had established a vast network of coal bunkering stations on all the major and most of the minor sea routes with her good quality coal. Until a similar network of oil bunkering stations could be built up, at least on the main trade routes, shipowners were naturally not prepared to invest in oil-burning ships for international trading. For coastal trading, there was not the same degree of risk that oil would not be available at the next port of call: take for instance the early development of oil-burning ships on the Caspian.

What was, perhaps, surprising was the reluctance of some tanker owners to invest in oil-burning ships. Here, one would have thought, was the ideal ship to use fuel oil, since not only did it carry oil, but always traded between oil ports. Even the Royal Dutch/Shell Group with their own availability of heavy crudes and, hence, fuel oil, did not convert all their fleet to oil until 1914. Shell had started to use fuel oil tankers in 1896. Many of the Group's pre-Great War tankers were equipped to burn either oil or coal, since fuel oil was only available at the loading port. These tankers could readily switch from one fuel to the other, even at sea. Eagle Oil's tankers of the early 1910s could do the same for the Atlantic trade. Many tankers at this time carried general cargo on their non-oil voyage legs and so had to call at non-oil ports. This fact made owners reluctant to rely completely on oil for bunkers. Most tanker owners waited until the 1910s before moving to fuel oil. Shipowners in general, left it until after the First World War. Only 3% of the world's merchant tonnage was oil-burning in 1914 and, of this, about half was under the US flag.

The slowness in switching from coal to oil at sea was fostered by the reluctance of Britain to lose her coal exports. Not only was coal one of the mainstays of the British economy, and bunkering coal exports an important element of coal trade, but these coal trades were a critical factor in whether the British tramp fleet could remain competitive in the face of cheaper flag tonnage. The British vessels had both these outward bound cargoes as well as the normal import trade to Northern Europe, while other flag vessels had only the one-way import trade open to them. On board ship there was also a resistance to change. Ships engineers could make side money when loading coal, as the measurement of exactly how much was taken onboard was not easy – with oil they could not play such games!

It was Marcus Samuel, the founder of Shell, who became the pioneer of "smokeless liquid fuel" for marine use. Samuel realised the potential of fuel oil almost as soon as it was found in the Far East, and he also needed to create outlets for his own company's heavy oil. His big barrier in developing this market was again the lack of oil bunkering stations. It was a chicken and egg problem. Without these stations, no owner would switch to oil, but without oil-burning ships there was not the economic incentive for him to create the necessary worldwide network of stations. If only he could convince one really big ship operator to convert, then he would have the market upon which to build his bunkering stations and other owners would automatically move to oil. Who better to convince than the biggest ship operator in the world, the British Navy! It did not turn out to be a simple task. The Lords of the Admiralty were not easily convinced. In 1903 some battleships were fitted out to test fuel oil. In 1906 a few more vessels were converted, but it was not until 1910, with the dangers of war becoming evident, that they took at last the final decision. Much to the chagrin of Samuel, the resulting lucrative fuel oil contract was not passed to him, but to the emerging Anglo-Persian Oil Company. Even so, it took until 1919 for the Anglo-Persian and the other big oil companies to begin to develop a worldwide network of bunkering stations. So again, it was not until well after the First World War that shipowners had guaranteed supplies of fuel oil throughout the world.

The steam engine, whether coal- or oil-fired, was not the only efficient marine propulsion unit around. The diesel engine had been developed for the ship early in the century. First it was tried in a canal barge in 1902 and then in a Russian-built tanker, the *Wandel*. Just like the beginnings of the coal-fired steam tanker, the *Wandel*, the first motor tanker was used on the Caspian Sea. The first deep sea motor tanker was the small, Dutch-built *Vulcanus*, of 1,215

DWT, owned by Shell, traded in the Far East and run on crude oil. She was delivered in 1910, but it took nearly 20 years more of development for the diesel engine to become generally accepted by tanker owners.

If the traditional owners had not had their hands forced by the growing competition from Norwegian tonnage, the introduction of the motor tanker would have been even slower. The Norwegians specifically built motor tankers. They realised their economic advantages. It was through them that the oil companies came to see that the diesel engine was best suited for long voyages and big vessels. By the early 1930s, more motor tankers were being ordered than steam tankers and by the Second World War, in 1938, 8m DWT of the total world tanker fleet of 16.1m DWT was diesel powered. For the Norwegian fleet of 3m DWT in this year 80% was motor, whilst 4m DWT or 50% of the British fleet and only 4.1m DWT or 10% of the US flag fleet was motor.

In its early days, the diesel unit was heavier and less reliable than the well tried and tested steam engine and was also more expensive. Diesel fuel was more costly than fuel oil. These disadvantages had to be weighed up against the lower fuel consumption of the diesel engine. By the early 1920s, improvements had made the large motor tankers 10%–20% cheaper than the oil-fired steam tanker. It was not just the diesel engine which was improved, but also the steam unit. The steam turbine superseded the old reciprocating engine, while the diesel engine was modified to burn cheap fuel oil. During the 1930s, the Japanese made great strides in developing the modern high speed diesel engine. As a result of these improvements, bunker consumption decreased considerably, and carrying capacity and speed increased tremendously. At the turn of the century, tanker speeds were around nine knots, but by the Second World War were up to an average of 11 knots, 22% higher, and a usual maximum of 13 knots. But some Japanese motor tankers, built for the Japanese Navy, had design speeds over 18 knots – the *Tatekawa Maru*, for instance, of 13,691 DWT built in 1935, set a new record at 20.5 knots while loaded.

Another advantage of diesel over steam was the lower weight of bunkers which had to be carried. In 1900, a 6,000 DWT steam tanker at nine knots consumed 40 tons of coal a day. In 1938, a 15,000 DWT tanker at 11 knots consumed 40 tons of oil a day if it was a steamship but only 15 tons a day if it was diesel. On the North Atlantic run from New York to London, the 1900-built tanker, therefore, needed some 15% of its deadweight set aside for bunkers, including some reserve supplies, but in 1938, the steam tanker needed only 4% of deadweight and the motor tanker only 2%, resulting in over a 10% gain in cargo carrying capacity. Allowing for additional gains in storage and handling space with the shift from coal to oil, the real increase was at least 15%.

It was not just speed and consumption which affected carrying power, but, with continuous improvements in construction methods and materials, classification societies allowed tankers to be loaded deeper in the water. A ship could

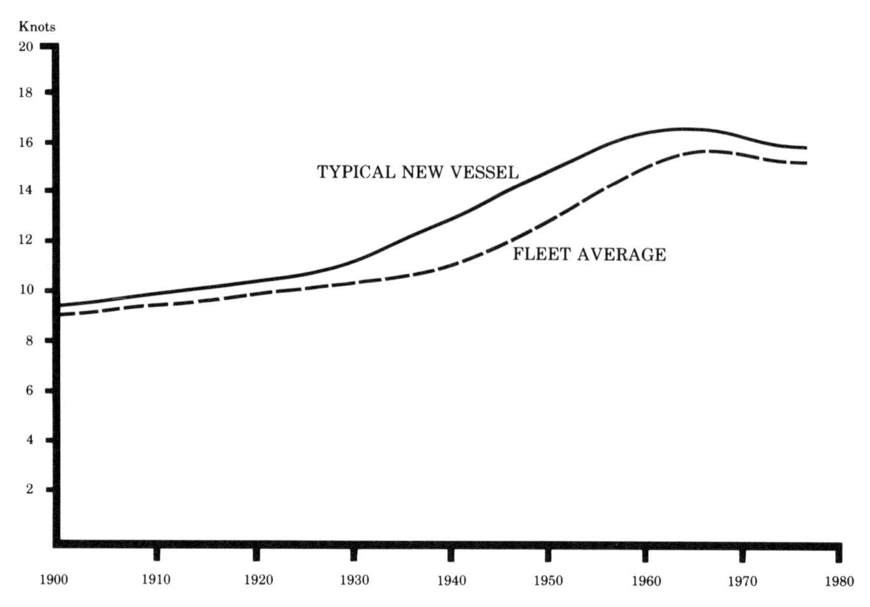

be loaded down to her "load line" or "Plimsoll line". This method of regulating the maximum tonnage of cargo on any ship had been in force since the late 19th century, when it had been introduced by Samuel Plimsoll of Lloyd's Register. In general, load lines were accepted by tanker operators at the beginning of this century, apart from those trading around the US coasts, where load line regulations did not come into force until 1930.

US coastal tankers could load over the normal safe limits accepted in the rest of the world and, in high freight markets, they did just that. However, the Load Line Convention of 1930 not only brought US coastal tankers under international regulations, but also recommended an increase of deadweight for any given tanker of 7% by allowing them to sink deeper into the water. Throughout the 1930s, tankers had their load lines recut as and when they came up for surveys. The carrying capacity of the world fleet gradually increased over the decade.

The following table, which shows the effect on the round voyage across the Atlantic (6,800 nautical miles), gives an idea of the overall increase in carrying power of the tanker fleet during this period.

With a real increase in carrying power of nearly 50% during this period, fewer tankers had to be built to cover tanker demand than would otherwise have been necessary. Although the consumers of oil did not gain much in the way of economies of scale from 1900 to the Second World War, they certainly benefited from these increases in efficiency.

Increase in tanker carrying power from 1900 to 1938

	1900	*1938*	*Change*
Speed	9 knots	11 knots	+22%
Round voyage time (US/Europe)	36 days	30 days	−17%
Number of voyages per year at 345 operating days/year	9.6 voy/yr	11.5 voy/yr	+20%
Units of pre-1930 DWT, assuming one per voyage	9.6 DWT units/yr	12.3 DWT units/yr	+28%
Units of carrying power, allowing for decreased bunker capacity	9.6 DWCT units/yr	14.1 DWCT units/yr	+47%

In 1861, it had cost 65 shillings per ton to have kerosine shipped from New York to London on the *Elizabeth Watts*, although the rate during the 1860s was normally as much as 100s. per ton. By the early 20th century the rate had declined to around 15s. per ton, and apart from a few short lived booms, gradually drifted down to under 10s. for the 1930s. These early years of the 20th century, therefore, saw a considerable change in tanker ownership, trade routes, design and efficiency. The world was now reliant on oil and, so, on tankers. The tanker industry had become a very important element of world shipping with a large and growing independent sector.

At its launch (February 1970) the biggest ship built in Britain: *Esso Northumbria* (253,000 tons) leaves the Tyne for dry dock in

BOOK III
THE AGE OF THE SUPERTANKER
(1938–1984)

A view of the Suez Canal, the new "road" from supplier to consumer, but eventually outgrown by the tanker trades.

The pipeline roads now carry oil across hundreds of miles on several continents. One of the first is shown under construction in Egypt.

14 THE FABULOUS MIDDLE EAST

The fortunes which were to be made out of Middle East oil were undreamed of when war broke out in 1939. Oil had already been found all round the Persian Gulf, but no one knew just how much lay under those inhospitable sands. In any case, many of the really big fields were discovered only a year or two before the war, and so had to wait until hostilities ended in 1945 to be exploited.

By 1939 Iraq, Bahrain, Saudi Arabia, Kuwait and Qatar had all been added to Iran as Middle East oil states, but only the first three, with Iran, had managed to export any oil by this date. Iraq and Bahrain began exporting in 1934, 22 years after the first Persian shipments, and Saudi Arabia in 1938. In total, these four were producing 15m tons in 1938, only some 6% of world production, whilst exports amounted to 13m tons or 15% of total world seaborne trade – the lion's share, around 75%, coming from Iran.

The reasons for the delay in developing the area were many, often political, sometimes economic and, of course, climatic. As early as 1909 when oil was being discovered in Persia, European and American interests were vying for stakes in Iraq, or Mesopotamia as it was then – part of the old Turkish empire. Just as an agreement was reached between all parties, the First World War broke out. After the war, Germany's share was taken up by France which, hand-in-hand with Britain, attempted to find oil. Great efforts were made to keep US oil companies out of the area. However, the pressure of the US

Government was too much and a year after oil was found in 1927, the American companies were reluctantly allowed in.

Political infighting by the major powers created delays in other areas. It also was not that easy to obtain exploration rights from the local rulers. The harsh terrain, the heat of the summer months, the sheer size of the Middle East – over half the area of the USA – and virtually nonexistent communications meant that delays were inevitable.

For example, it took seven years to link the Iraqi oil fields to export terminals. Hundreds of miles from either the Mediterranean or the Persian Gulf, a major construction project to get to deep water was inevitable. With Europe as the natural market, a 530 mile pipeline route to the Eastern Mediterranean was eventually chosen.

The discoveries around the Persian Gulf created problems of their own, but distance from the sea was not one of them. The huge fields of Kuwait and Saudi Arabia, like "bottomless pits of oil", were right by the sea, and the unit cost of producing in the area was guaranteed to be the lowest in the world.

By the end of the Second World War, all five US major oil companies (Chevron, Esso, Gulf, Mobil and Texaco) plus the two European-based majors (Royal Dutch/Shell and BP) were well established throughout the region. These seven completely dominated production. Other companies had stakes in Middle East oil, CFP for France, and lesser American oil companies such as Getty, but they held only minor interests. Since Venezuela was also tied up by most of these seven majors, the simple fact of life was that world oil production and, for that matter, refining and retail outlets, outside North America and the Communist world were under their control – with very few exceptions!

Quietly, but surely, the world of oil was changed. Out of the monopolistic stranglehold of Rockefeller and the Standard had risen the oligopolistic and, in some respects, even more powerful union of the "seven sisters". Just as Rockefeller had used his dominance to dictate availability and price, so now did the seven majors. Their cartel was, for the most time, unofficial, but its effect was indisputable.

Rockefeller had not bothered with controlling world oil from production, but via distribution and sales. The majors dominated all three elements. At least they did until the 1960s, when the rules of the game began to change. First they lost control over crude oil costs, then in the 1970s over production, but this still left them in charge of the only two elements that Rockefeller worried about – distribution and sales – the real power base. If they worked together, that is.

Much has been written about the cartel of the majors during this period and the details are not really relevant to this story. Suffice to say that for tankers, the cooperation between the majors in developing joint export and import terminals, exchanging ideas and technology, did much good. Just as the stability created by Rockefeller helped the tanker industry to develop during the last decades of the 19th century, so now did the seven sisters foster a similar atmosphere, also to the benefit of the tanker world.

The reason why the majors began to lose their grip on world oil production went back to the years around the Second World War. Between the wars, US production had managed to maintain a growth rate similar to that of US consumption, but no more. There were periodic worries over the ability of the industry to find enough oil to satisfy future demand and hence a continual search abroad for new supplies by the US majors, aided and abetted by the US Government.

Once the Second World War was over, although US production continued to grow, consumption now began to outstrip it. By 1948, the USA had become a net importer of oil. Such a thing had not been known for over 100 years, when Young of Britain was exporting to America across the Atlantic.

Within the Western Hemisphere, Venezuelan exports could not keep up with the post-war boom in US consumption. Canada exported overland what she could, but still the US needed more and inevitably looked to the Middle East. Here there were huge fields which promised to be cheap, politically controllable and hence highly profitable, especially when compared with the ever escalating cost of domestic US crudes.

Although the prospects of importing Middle East oil into the States was attractive on paper, the situation was not quite as simple in practice; the big producers in the Middle East – the majors – were in many cases also big producers in the USA and Venezuela. A massive import of Middle East oil into the USA would simply have replaced profitable low cost US production, since state control tended to support high cost, marginal production. Alternatively, it would have displaced profitable Venezuelan production and so the net effect would have been minimal.

Not all the majors were in the same position and, for some, protection of the US market was far less important than for others. BP, for instance, was not in the US or Venezuela. Together with Gulf Oil, it shared the immense resources of Kuwait and so, theoretically, had nothing to lose from exporting to the USA. Gulf, on balance, probably also stood to gain more from importing Middle East oil into the States, whereas the situation for the other five, particularly Esso and Shell, tended to be the reverse.

BREAKDOWN OF WORLD CRUDE OIL PRODUCTION

	USA	Other W. Hemi	Russia	Middle East	Africa	Other E. Hemi	Total
1940	63%	16%	10%	4%	—	7%	100%
1950	53%	20%	7%	16%	1%	3%	100%
1960	35%	21%	14%	24%	1%	5%	100%
1970	23%	15%	15%	29%	10%	8%	100%
1980	16%	12%	20%	30%	10%	12%	100%
1982	18%	14%	22%	23%	8%	15%	100%

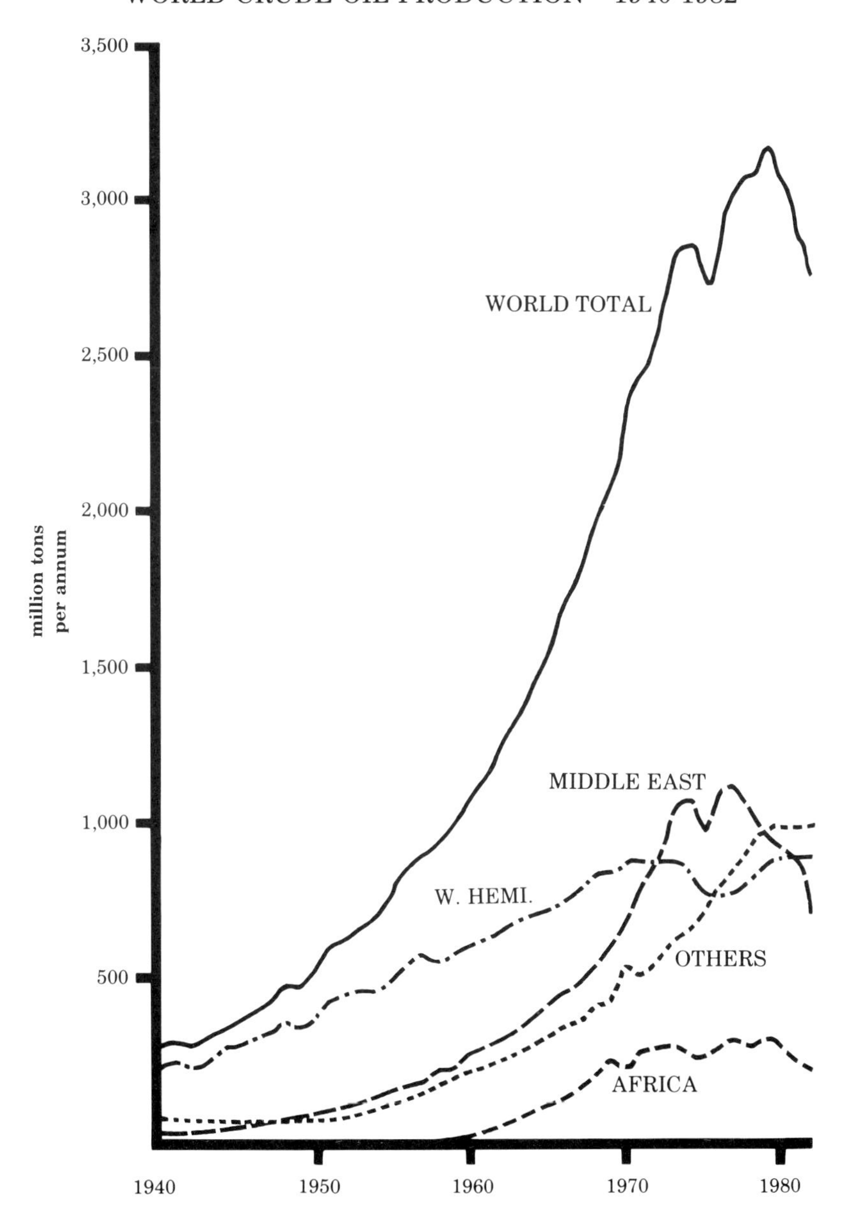
WORLD CRUDE OIL PRODUCTION—1940-1982
3,500
3,000
2,500
2,000
1,500
1,000
500
million tons
per annum
WORLD TOTAL
MIDDLE EAST
W. HEMI.
OTHERS
AFRICA
1940
1950
1960
1970
1980

In 1955, the US price of imported Middle East oil was around $3.00 per barrel ($1.93 fob Persian Gulf plus $1.10 per barrel freight), whereas US crudes were on average $2.77 per barrel at well head and hence also around $3.00 per barrel delivered to New York. For a company producing in the Middle East, the cost in the Persian Gulf was, however, only around $0.40 at this time and so no more than $1.50 delivered to New York.

The potential profit margin of $1.50 per barrel, or over $10 a ton, was just immense. That is except during the early 1950s when the Korean War pushed tanker rates up to levels four times what they had been in the late 1940s. In 1951, therefore, the import cost for Middle East producers had shot up to over $3.00 per barrel, but by the mid-1950s, freight rates had again dropped and the economic pressures were back on certain companies to sell Middle East oil into the USA.

The US market was still a wide mix of both big and small oil companies and it was principally the independent refiners who were at least risk by importing Middle East oil and stood to gain a lot if they could get it cheap. With such huge profit margins, one would have expected one of the Middle East producers to cut prices so that the delivered price in the USA was below that of domestic crudes and, hence, for Middle East exports to boom. In practice, prices in the Persian Gulf rose throughout the 1950s and imports into the US stagnated at around 15m tons a year for most of the decade.

The logical conclusion to be drawn from this is that the majors were not freely competing with each other. Perhaps, therefore, massive cut-price Middle East imports into the States were never a real threat. However, the small US producers and the US Government did not see it like that at the time and were very worried over the prospect of a flood of cheap Middle East oil in the States.

With the Cold War very much in evidence, the US Government had no desire to see the proportion of the country's oil consumption covered from "unreliable sources" rise too high. Thus, with pressure from domestic producers, in 1954 and again in 1959, the US Government tried to get companies to reduce imports voluntarily. Some did but, in particular, the independents did not. So in 1959, the Government introduced oil import quotas, freezing the proportion of US oil imports to around the 1959 level.

To put this action in context, during the years 1954 to 1959 Middle East imports ranged from 11m to 19m tons a year and were never more than 20% of total US oil imports. With oil imports accounting for only 15% to 20% of total oil consumption, they never rose above 4% of US consumption. Added to this, there was little indication that the majors were prepared to undertake a price war in order to swamp the USA with Middle East oil, but this was not the perspective that those in power in the USA were prepared to see.

In retrospect, this was one of the most crucial events in the whole history of both oil and tankers. From it cascaded a torrent of crises over the next 20 years. Probably many would have happened in any case, but certainly not all. This one action by the US Government was the beginning of the end of cheap oil

MIDDLE EAST: LOADING TERMINALS AND PIPELINE LINKS TO CRUDE OIL PRODUCTION AREAS

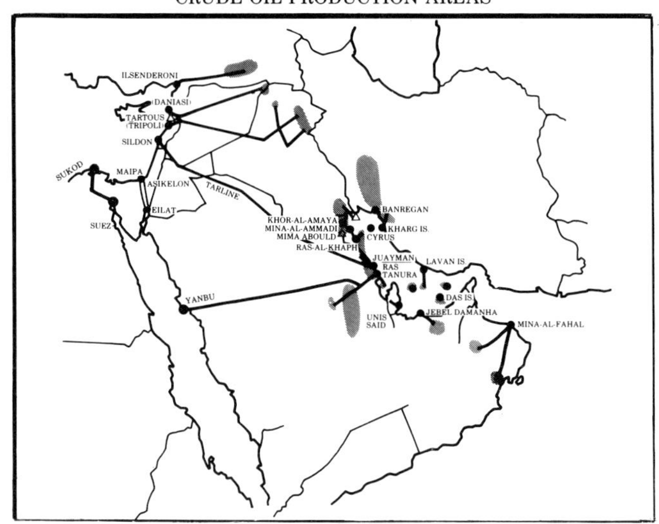

AFRICA: LOADING TERMINALS AND PIPELINE LINKS TO CRUDE OIL PRODUCTION AREAS

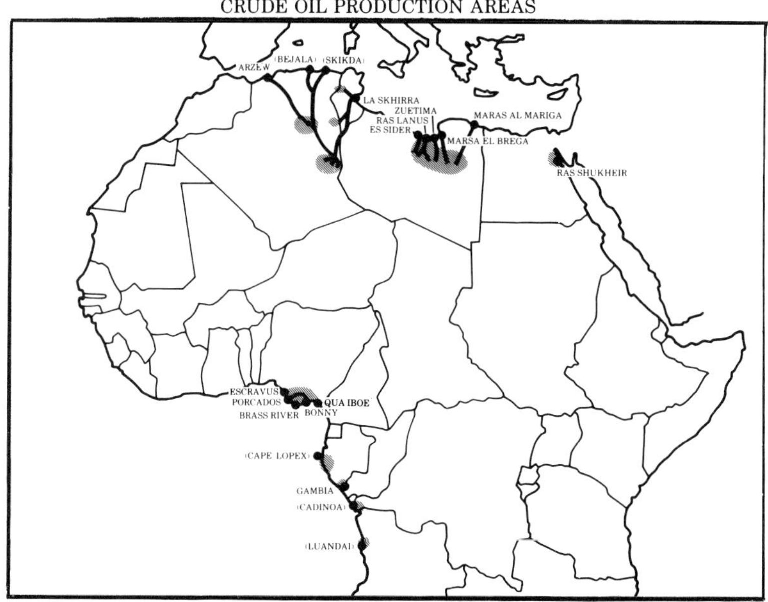

KEY TO MAPS: ● MAJOR CRUDE OIL TERMINALS

CRUDE OIL PRODUCTION AREAS

—— MAJOR CRUDE OIL PIPELINES

throughout the world. Whether it was the real cause of all the events to come is debatable and, to some extent, academic. What was important was that many people at the time, and later, saw it as an unprovoked and unilateral attack on free world oil trade by the most powerful of nations.

As the US had been slowly shutting her door on imported oil during the 1950s, production in the Middle East had begun to accelerate. For most of the decade, the majors had succeeded in stage-managing the oil market in such a way that supply was always slightly less than demand, and so prices rose. But towards the end of the decade, with the US market no longer available, output began to outstrip international demand and prices weakened – much to the concern of Middle East and Caribbean producing governments.

Arabian light crude oil (Saudi Arabian) – posted price (fob the Persian Gulf)

1950	$1.75 per barrel
1953	$1.93 per barrel
1957	$2.08 per barrel
1959	$1.90 per barrel
1960	$1.80 per barrel

They saw the American Government's action as a direct blow to their exports and their only source of foreign earnings. One year after the imposition of US import quotas, they banded together to form OPEC, the Organisation of Petroleum Exporting Countries. This organisation's prime role was to stop the further deterioration of oil prices, and it froze the official price of crude on which its member states calculated their taxes and royalties – the posted price.

Overnight the oil market had been turned upside down. As well as the huge reserves of Middle East oil having to look to other markets than the USA, the majors no longer controlled the cost of their non-US oil production. Now that the OPEC members had tasted power in the face of the majors, they individually continued to exert pressure for increases in their own crude oil posted prices, or alternatively (or additionally) higher liftings to push up their state revenues.

The majors resisted any attempts to raise posted prices, but were prepared to increase exports (and also pay higher taxes per barrel). As more and more oil was pushed on the market, the real market price fell well under the frozen posted price, cutting into the once obese, but still plump, profits of the majors. The only way for them to maintain profits was to sell more and this only depressed the price further. The 1960s became a crazy merry-go-round with OPEC chasing the majors, chasing prices, chasing profits, chasing OPEC.

It is said that most of the considerable investment made by BP in refining and marketing refined products via retail outlets during this period was simply to keep the Shah of Iran happy. He was continually pushing for higher revenues and this meant higher exports and the only way BP could do this was by expanding its downsteam activities. In return, BP increased its availability of Iranian crude to sell on the open market and it was here, in the crude oil sale market, that BP made all its profits, not in the downstream refining and retailing.

By the late 1960s, the cost of Middle East oil to the majors rose to around $1.00 per barrel and the market price had fallen to $1.20, or even lower in certain large deals. So in 10 years, the actual price of oil had fallen dramatically by some 40%, or nearer 60% if allowance is made for inflation.

Just as economic forces pushed down the price of oil, so similar forces created a growing demand for it in response. The Second World War had destroyed much of Western Europe's coal industry and oil was the only immediately available alternative. Similarly, in Japan, coal mines could not cover the country's rapidly growing energy demand in the post war years. With oil so cheap, and getting cheaper all the time, the markets in these two areas expanded with traditional coal consumers switching to oil and new ones being created on the back of ridiculously cheap energy.

As the following table shows, the move from coal to oil in both Western Europe and Japan was extraordinary.

Primary energy consumption in the major areas

	USA			*Western Europe*			*Japan*		
	Oil	*Solid*	*Others*	*Oil*	*Solid*	*Others*	*Oil*	*Solid*	*Others*
1950	42%	38%	20%	15%	75%	10%	7%	80%	15%
1960	46%	24%	30%	29%	55%	16%	36%	49%	15%
1970	44%	21%	35%	56%	28%	16%	70%	22%	8%
1980	43%	22%	35%	53%	21%	26%	66%	16%	18%

(Note: others include natural gas, nuclear, etc. Source: *BP Statistical Review of World Energy*)

In the 20 years from 1950 to 1970, the roles of coal and oil in these two areas had effectively been reversed. Nothing could compete with the cheapness of Middle East oil. Coal moved from being the prime to being the reserve energy resource, and had to fight to maintain a share against a background of rising labour costs at the coal face and falling oil prices.

The cheapness of oil was a great bonus to Western Europe and Japan. Inadvertently, the USA had created the biggest aid programme possible to the war-shattered industries of these areas. Cut price and readily available energy was handed to them on a plate by the US who slammed the door shut to the benefits of the Persian Gulf. No wonder that these two areas not only turned away from coal to oil, but that they also underwent a huge surge in overall energy consumption, only to add further to their oil import requirements.

BREAKDOWN OF WESTERN EUROPEAN TOTAL ENERGY CONSUMPTION

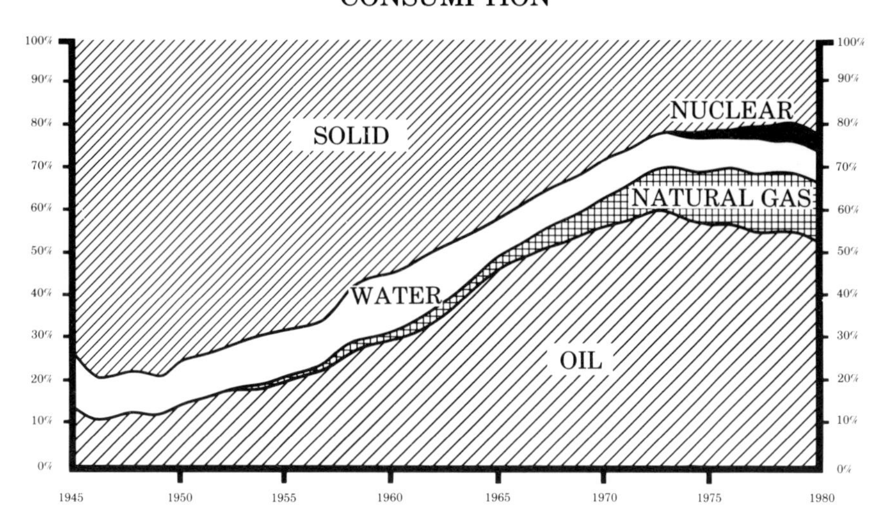

BREAKDOWN OF JAPANESE TOTAL ENERGY CONSUMPTION

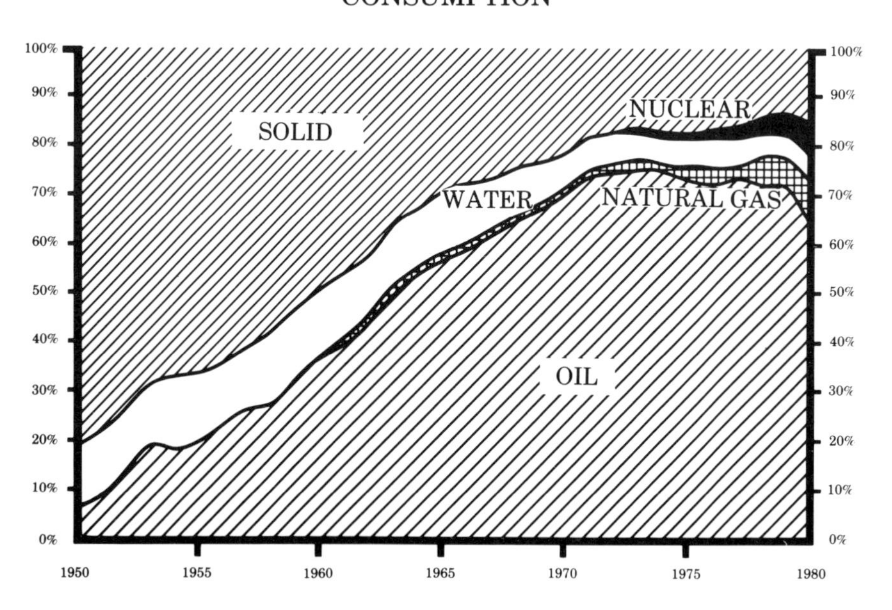

By 1938, Western Europe was importing 38m tons of oil a year, by 1950 the figure had nearly doubled to 60m tons, by 1960 it had more than tripled to 200m tons, and tripled again by 1970 to 636m tons, but then grew very little so that by 1978 it stood at 648m tons a year, and by 1980 had actually declined to 589m tons a year. The picture in Japan was even more spectacular. In 1938, she was only importing around 4m tons a year, by 1950 still only some 6m, but by 1960 five times more at 38m, by 1970 nearly six times more at 213m tons and then again only a very modest growth through the 1970s to 263m tons a year by 1978, and a decline to 246m tons a year by 1980.

The years up to 1970 were *the* growth years. Never had seaborne oil demand grown so fast and to such heights, nor is it likely that it will ever see such growth rates again. The years following 1970 were very different for oil demand and are so important to this story that they are dealt with separately in a later chapter. So for now only the glorious 1950s and 1960s need be looked at – the golden years for oil shipments and the tanker industry.

During these years up to 1970, the Middle East was not the only area to be developed. Exploration continued in both Venezuela and Indonesia and whilst additional fields were discovered, development was not spectactular. The big new area to be opened up was Africa.

Oil had been known about in both North and West Africa well before the First World War, but it was not until the 1950s that any large scale finds were made. The discovery of the Hassi Messaoud fields in the Algerian Sahara in 1956 was the first sign of the untapped wealth in North Africa. By 1959, Esso had found Zelten in Libya. Even earlier, in 1955, Shell and BP had discovered oil in Nigeria and so in the late 1950s, exports from these new finds in North and West Africa began to come on the market.

The majors had again got in first but, unlike the Middle East, were not allowed to maintain a monopoly. Non-major American and Western European oil companies were encouraged to explore in Libya, often in consortia with the majors. This example was followed in West Africa, and, as new territories were opened up for exploration and oil found, names other than the big seven were added to the list of international oil producers and tanker owners – Occidental, Marathon, Continental, Amerada, Amoco and so on.

Africa, therefore, brought diversity to the oil world in more ways than one, but it failed to live up to its expectations. In the 1960s as the true magnitude of the Middle East was being appreciated, people thought that Africa might also hold the same immense volumes of oil. "No one knew how large the Middle East was to begin with", they argued, "so why should Africa not be just as large?" Why not indeed. By the time 1970 came along, it was becoming clear that the reason was simply that the oil was just not there.

African production in total never reached more than a third of Middle East output. By 1970 the big growth was over. Many of its fields could not be expanded and some were even declining. Africa helped Western Europe in its mad hunger for oil during the 1960s, but by the 1970s could no longer maintain the pace of development and output stagnated.

In the 25 years from 1945 to 1970, the oil industry had undergone dramatic structural changes. The US switched from being the centre of the oil world to a domestic industry maintained by import barriers. The Middle East became the centre of world production, exports and hence tanker loadings, and Western Europe the centre of the international operations of the majors and the oil market, oil imports and tanker discharges. The power of the seven majors was severely weakened in the area of crude oil production, to be replaced by that of OPEC. However, the control by the majors over international distribution, sales and tanker trades remained. But of all changes, the most visible to the tanker world was that of the 10 fold leap in the volume of trade, from 129m tons in 1939 to 1,327m tons in 1970, an average growth rate of 7.8% per year for the full 31 years.

The Arabian-American Oil Company's desert pipeline to the Ras Tanura refinery and tanker terminal.

15 ECONOMIES OF SCALE

One would be hard pressed to find an area more remote from both Western Europe and Japan than the Persian Gulf. The huge distances from these, plus the constantly powerful growth of trade out of this region, combined to create a whole new set of economic rules not only for the tanker world, but also for the international oil industry.

The growth of Persian Gulf exports was tremendous during the 1950s and 1960s, around 11% per year on average for the full 20 years. In total, shipments of oil from this one area nearly added up to all other international seaborne trades of goods, and by 1970 accounted for 43% of world seaborne oil trade, including US coastal movements.

Up to 1960, the only new export area was the Middle East with terminals in both the Eastern Mediterranean and the Persian Gulf. Northern Iraqi crude was exported from the Eastern Mediterranean terminals of Tripoli and Banias and in December 1950 TAPLINE, the 1,067 mile long pipeline from the immense oil fields in the Eastern Province of Saudi Arabia to Sidon in the Lebanon was opened. All other Middle East oil had to be shipped from the Persian Gulf. During the 1960s, North and West Africa came on the scene, but these did little to change voyage lengths. It was trades from the Persian Gulf which radically altered the distances that tankers had to sail.

Pre-Second World War tanker distances were around the 2,000 to 4,000 mile range. But Persian Gulf routes were 50% to 100% longer at 4,000 to 8,000 miles, and that was using the Suez Canal for western trades. Via the Cape of Good Hope, they were nearly three times as long at 11,000 to 12,000 miles.

Just as the reduction in voyage lengths between the wars had tended to restrict the economics of moving to larger vessels, now the reverse occurred. The longer voyage lengths and higher volumes created lower costs per ton of cargo at sea and made it easier for larger vessels to overcome the extra costs they incurred in port, such as deeper and more frequent dredging, bigger tugs, jetties and land storage. The development of Persian Gulf exports, therefore, directly created pressure to increase tanker sizes right through the 1950s, the 1960s and into the 1970s as more and more of this long haul oil came available for shipment.

World seaborne oil trade (million tons a year)

	Middle East			*Other international*	*US coastal*	*World total*	*PG % of total*
	E Med	*PG*	*Total*				
1938	4	9	13	67	49	129	7%
1950	6	72	78	99	78	255	28%
1960	44	190	234	200	94	528	36%
1970	75	566	641	592	94	1327	43%

Typical single voyage distance (nautical miles)

From: / To:	*North West Europe*	*Southern Europe*	*Japan*	*USEC*
Caribbean	4,200	4,600		1,700
S E Asia			3,000	
N Africa	2,500	800		4,400
W Africa	4,500	4,500		5,100
E Med	3,400	1,400		5,200
P G – Suez	6,500	4,400	6,700	8,300
Cape	11,300	11,200		11,900

Although the desire may have been there to build bigger and bigger vessels, it did not follow that there was automatically the ability. The pre-war oil cargoes had been refined products from the Persian Gulf, while from the Eastern Mediterranean, crude oil. As was seen in the years up to the Second World War, the shipments of refined products inhibited the use of the largest of vessels. So in the post-war era, there had to be a re-orientation of the oil industry from "source" located refineries to "market" located plants to enable

COMPARATIVE COSTS OF TRANSPORTING CRUDE OIL FROM KUWAIT TO ROTTERDAM IN 1969

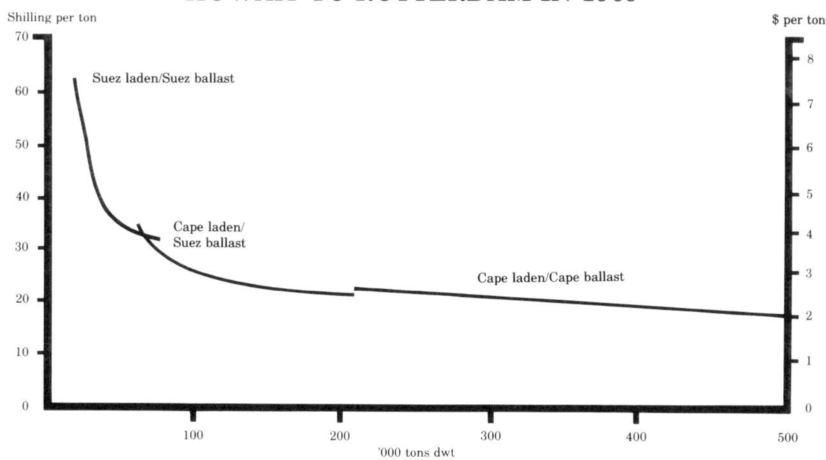

Source: Royal Dutch Shell Group — "Shell Briefing Service"

crude rather than refined to be shipped from the Persian Gulf.

For Europe, and for that matter for Japan, the import of oil after the war was a major drain on dollar reserves. Governments, therefore, actively encouraged the development of domestic refining in Europe with the assistance of cheap finance and, in Japan, through US Government pressures with joint ventures with US oil companies. This minimised the cost of importing oil by bringing in the raw material, rather than processed oil.

For the oil industry, the economic equation was little different to that looked at in 1875 when the first crude oil pipeline was built to the US East Coast. The economies of scale and simplicity enjoyed by shipping one grade of cargo – crude – had to offset the diseconomies of shipping and handling the non-revenue earning "refinery fuel and loss". In addition, the natural resistance to change had to be overcome, for nearly all the majors had invested in "source" located refining in the Persian Gulf and a switch to "market" plants meant a re-orientation of each company's supply strategy.

In 1949, Persian Gulf refinery output was significantly more than that of the whole of Western Europe's, at 38m tons compared with only 27m tons in Europe. BP had very heavily invested in the area, with its Iranian refinery at Abadan becoming the largest refinery in the world in 1951. The American majors had built plants at both Bahrain and Ras Tanura, in Saudi Arabia. As early as 1951, Western Europe was refining more oil than the Persian Gulf, 57m tons a year compared with only 33m tons from the Middle East: refineries were being developed all round the coast of both north and southern Europe at suitable deepwater ports.

This rapid change in the balance between Middle East and European refining was by no means just due to economic pressures. Politics had reared its ugly head once more, this time in Iran. If there had been any resistance to change before the Iranian crisis, there was certainly little after.

In 1948, the Anglo-Iranian Oil Company (the old BP) began to revise the terms of its concession with the Iranian Government. Things did not go well for the company and in 1951 the Iranian Government, under Prime Minister Mossadegh, nationalised its assets. The company refused to accept this and withdrew all its staff from the oil fields and the Abadan refinery. The other majors backed up this action and boycotted Iranian oil on the international market.

For BP, these events were traumatic. It was forced immediately to rethink its strategy and to opt for market-located refining in the future. For the oil industry, the Middle East was no longer the stable area it had been.

The situation was resolved in 1954, when Mossadegh was ousted and the Shah signed a new oil agreement. BP lost its sole rights to Iranian oil and "the Consortium" was set up. With the assistance of the US Government, the inevitable percentage of Iran oil fields was allocated to the US majors, together with Shell and CFP. Memories of Mexico and the nationalisation there were not so old, and the international oil industry carefully re-evaluated its attitudes towards Middle East oil and where best to invest capital.

Following Abadan, there must have been a temptation for the majors to view Middle East oil on a short term basis. Get the oil out now, rather than later – another push in the direction of higher Middle East production and faster tanker demand growth. For the producing governments, the feeling of exploitation must have been added to: OPEC did not evolve overnight just in response to the US oil import quota system. Nationalism had been growing in the Middle East for many years.

When oil began to be loaded at Iran's Kharg Island again in October 1954, the international oil world had already changed irrevocably. The majors now knew that market refineries were the only safe solution. On top of the simple economic facts was added security. In Europe, their refineries would not be nationalised. With market located plants, they would have much greater flexibility if one oil producing country stopped production, for crude exports from others could be switched into the lost trades; products being never as easy to switch from one market to another due to tight quality specifications in each market. Crude oil transportation was the answer and crude oil tankers had to be built.

The second Middle East crisis of the '50s – Suez – only helped to emphasise how important the security angle really was. President Nasser of Egypt had been trying to get the USA and the UK to finance the Aswan High Dam as the essential key element of his country's development plan. These plans failed and in 1956 Nasser nationalised the Suez Canal in order to finance the dam from its revenue. Later the same year Britain and France attempted to take over the canal by force, but without the necessary American support, this action was a failure.

As a result of the Anglo-French military action, Nasser blocked the canal and the Syrians blew up the pipelines taking Iraqi crude to the Eastern Mediterranean. The canal stayed closed from October 1956 to March 1957, and the pipelines from November 1956. The effect on the international oil supply pattern was immediate. The throughput of the wholly-owned American pipeline from Saudi Arabia, TAPLINE, to the Eastern Mediterranean was diverted to Europe, as were refined products exports from the Western Hemisphere. Shipments from the Persian Gulf had to be routed round the Cape. Europe survived, but her dependence upon stability in the Middle East was obvious for all to see.

The strength and co-operation of the majors ensured that the effects of these two crises were minimised for Europe and this co-operation did not finish once the crises were over. In building up the crude oil export and import facilities around the world, plus the necessary market-located refining capacity, many projects were undertaken jointly by the majors, whether port developments, tank farms or refinery developments. It is all too easy to point to the bad sides of the seven sisters – market sharing, price fixing, exploitation – but too often forgotten is the magnificently efficient international distribution system designed and set up jointly by them during these years.

Crude oil production was controlled by them and efficiently regulated. Export liftings were run by them and the individual requirements of world crude oil buyers co-ordinated by them. Joint working groups assisted individual port authorities to plan and finance channel dredging, berths, tugs and other services. The majors set up joint crude oil pipelines all over Western Europe, built and ran refineries both separately and together, even marketing jointly in certain areas.

In many instances, there were not seven sisters, but one all-embracing mother. The international oil supply network set up by them was highly efficient and tankers were an integral part of this co-ordinated world scheme. The negative side of their co-operation was to be seen in the oil market; but in the tanker market, only the positive was experienced.

As seaborne trade grew, so did market-located refining and crude oil tanker requirements. The opportunities to use bigger vessels expanded and in the 30 odd years from 1938 to 1970 tanker sizes increased by the incredible factor of 100, from 20,000 DWT to 200,000 DWT and by 1976, the first half million-tonner had been delivered.

The growth in the maximum size of tankers even outpaced the ability of the industry to find new superlatives to describe the new and larger classes. By the mid-'50s, designs were up to "supertankers" of 50/70,000 DWT. By the late '50s, "mammoths" of 100,000 DWT were being contemplated. In the early '60s, "giants" of 130,000 DWT were actually being built. By the mid '60s, the first generation VLCCs or Very Large Crude Carriers were being ordered, initially of 175,000 DWT, but changed to 210,000 DWT under construction. In the '70s, there were second and third generations of VLCCs or Ultra Large Crude Carriers of 350,000 DWT. When the 500,000 DWT barrier was eventually broken, in the second half of the '70s, there were no more superlatives left and it as simpler just to go back to calling these beasts "supertankers".

By far the most important trades for these supertankers were to North and South Europe from the Persian Gulf, followed by those to Japan. The development of refineries in Western Europe was centred around a few big continental ports, or along major trunk pipelines from these ports into the hinterland and to industrial areas like the Ruhr in Germany.

The five European trunk ports, Rotterdam (Netherlands), Wilhelmshaven (West Germany), Le Havre (Northern France), Lavera (Southern France), Genoa and Trieste (Italy) accounted for well over 50% of all of Western Europe's crude oil imports by the '70s including that of the UK and Scandinavia. All fed major inland pipeline networks and most had huge refining complexes around them. Rotterdam alone accounted for over 20% of Europe's total oil imports.

In addition to direct full shipments in supertankers, these huge vessels were discharged in two, or even three ports in Europe to get over expensive dredging projects. Berthing at the deepest port took place first. Similarly in the Persian Gulf, multi-port loading became a regular feature so as to minimise the cost of loading facilities and overcome constraints of parcel size; two 100,000 ton deliveries of different grades of crude could be loaded into one 200,000-tonner for either one or two European refineries.

In order to maximise the use of the biggest of tankers, the majors developed transhipment terminals in Europe, notably at Rotterdam and Bantry Bay in Ireland. 300/500,000-tonners could be used on the long haul from the Gulf and small 70/120,000s for delivery to limited draft European refineries. Shell, BP and Exxon all developed systems of off-loading part cargoes from VLCCs at sea into smaller, specially converted, tankers as yet another way to maximise the use of these giants.

In Japan co-ordinated development was much easier than in Europe, being a single country with a strong civil service machine. Japan's industry is concentrated on the main island's southern shores and it was here that key tanker ports were developed. By far the most important area became Tokyo Bay, with various terminals accounting for some 40% of total Japanese crude oil imports. Other major ports like Yokkaichi, Mizushima, Sakai and Shimotsu also grew up for big tankers, each accounting for up to 10% of crude imports. Trades to Europe were constrained by Suez, when open, whilst to Japan by the Malacca Strait. Only fully laden 260,000-tonners could pass through the Malaccan waterway and so virtually all Japanese terminals were developed to accommodate this size and no larger. There was no multi-port discharging in Japan.

There *was* transhipment, but at only one port, Kiire. Not too surprisingly two

WESTERN EUROPE: MAJOR DISCHARGE TERMINALS AND PIPELINE LINKS TO REFINING AREAS

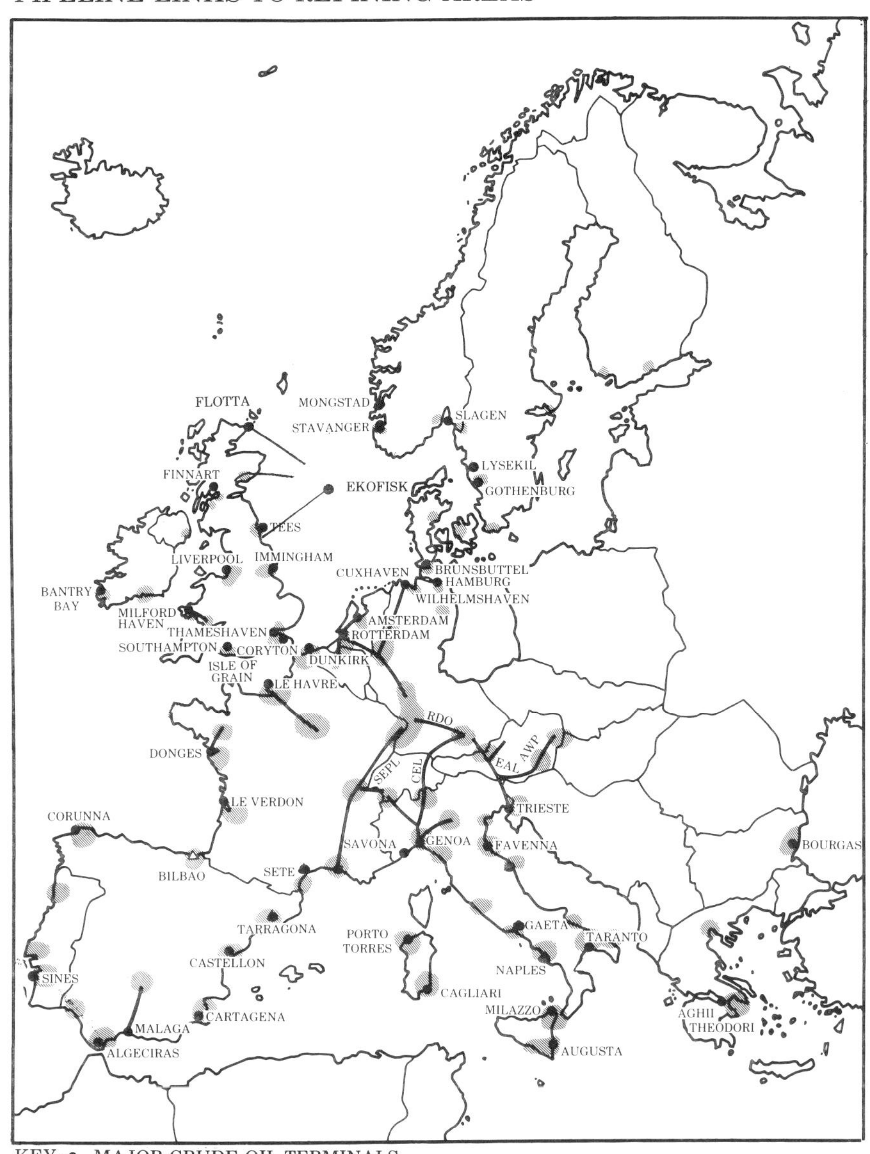

KEY: • MAJOR CRUDE OIL TERMINALS

REFINING AREAS

MAJOR CRUDE OIL PIPELINES

of the largest majors, Exxon and Mobil, were involved and here 500,000-tonners could discharge their Middle East cargoes. However, these ULCCs had to divert, loaded, 1,000 miles through the Lombok Strait and then return in ballast via the Malacca.

JAPAN: MAJOR DISCHARGE TERMINALS AND REFINING AREAS

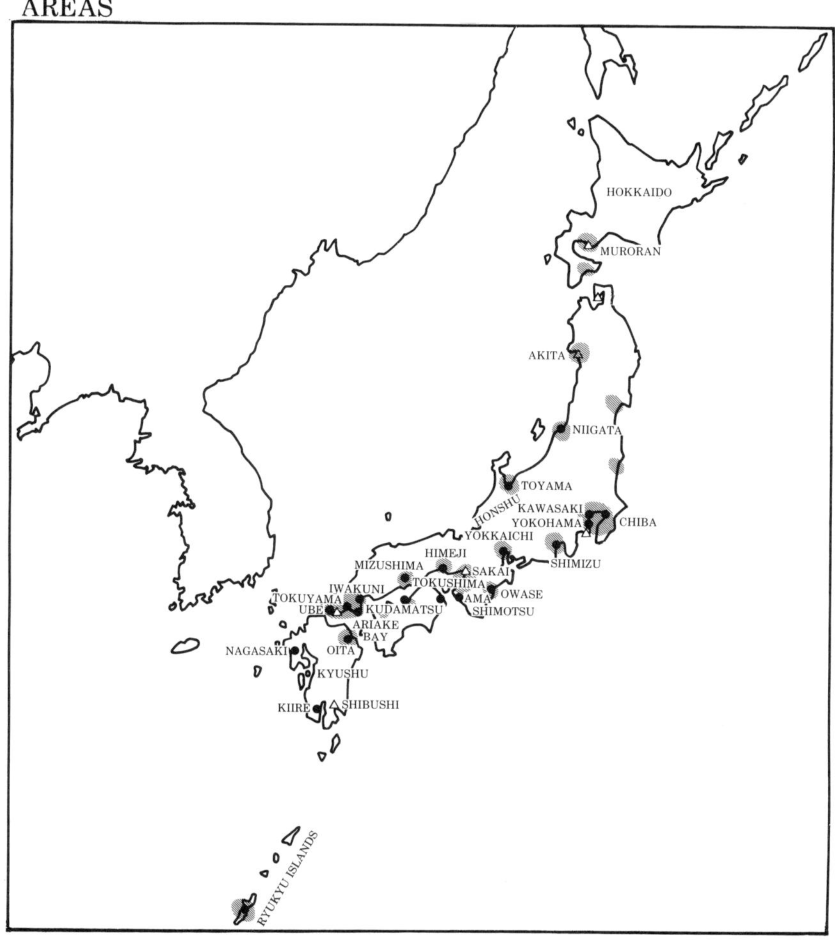

KEY: ● MAJOR CRUDE OIL TERMINALS

REFINING AREAS

In addition to the tremendous and constant growth in long haul oil trades during these years, there was another major boost to the development of the supertanker in the 1960s: the second closure of Suez. In June 1967 hostilities broke out between Israel and Egypt, resulting in the closure of the canal until June 1975. All tanker trades to the west suddenly had to be rerouted around the Cape and demand went up over night by nearly 70% on these trades and so pushed up world tanker demand by over 20%.

Just as in the other post war crises, the Korean war, Abadan and the first Suez closure, the tanker market reacted immediately and rates shot up. This time they did not fall back quickly. Owners with tankers free for charter made a killing. The majors and some large independents were already looking to big tankers which would be cheap enough to take the Cape route on both legs of their journey to Europe and so save the canal dues. As a direct reaction to the high market, the majors increased the size of their vessels on order and went into a big new buildings programme of VLCCs. With the profits made on the booming market, the independents did likewise.

World Tanker Fleet from 1900 to 1980
(million DWT)

	under 25,000 DWT	*25,000 to 65,000 DWT*	*65,000 to 205,000 DWT*	*205,000 DWT plus*	*Total*
1900	0.4	—	—	—	0.4
1938	16.6	—	—	—	16.6
1950	26.1	1.5	—	—	27.6
1960	36.8	25.9	1.3	—	64.0
1970	28.3	49.9	48.8	28.7	155.7
1980	14.1	40.7	85.5	184.5	324.8

Source: 1938 and later BP Statistical Review of World Energy

There was great uncertainty over when the Suez Canal would reopen. However, as the VLCC was too large to transit the canal either loaded or in ballast, the problem over the timing of any reopening was minimised. When Suez did eventually reopen, the tanker world had changed from one highly dependent upon the canal to one being virtually independent of it. It was the canal which had to readjust to the tanker industry in the late '70s, not the other way about. Egypt was, therefore, forced to consider dredging and widening the canal firstly for fully laden 150,000-tonners, which was completed in 1980, also allowing 370,000 DWT ships through in ballast. Plans for fully laden 260,000 DWT and 700,000 DWT in ballast have had to be shelved for the time being.

In 1900, seaborne oil trades added up to nearly 5m tons and not much more than 1% of world seaborne trade. By 1937, international oil trades had risen to 105m tons a year, or some 20% of world seaborne trade. By 1950, oil's importance had grown to just under 40%, and by 1970 to 55%. In response to

SUEZ CANAL DEVELOPMENT

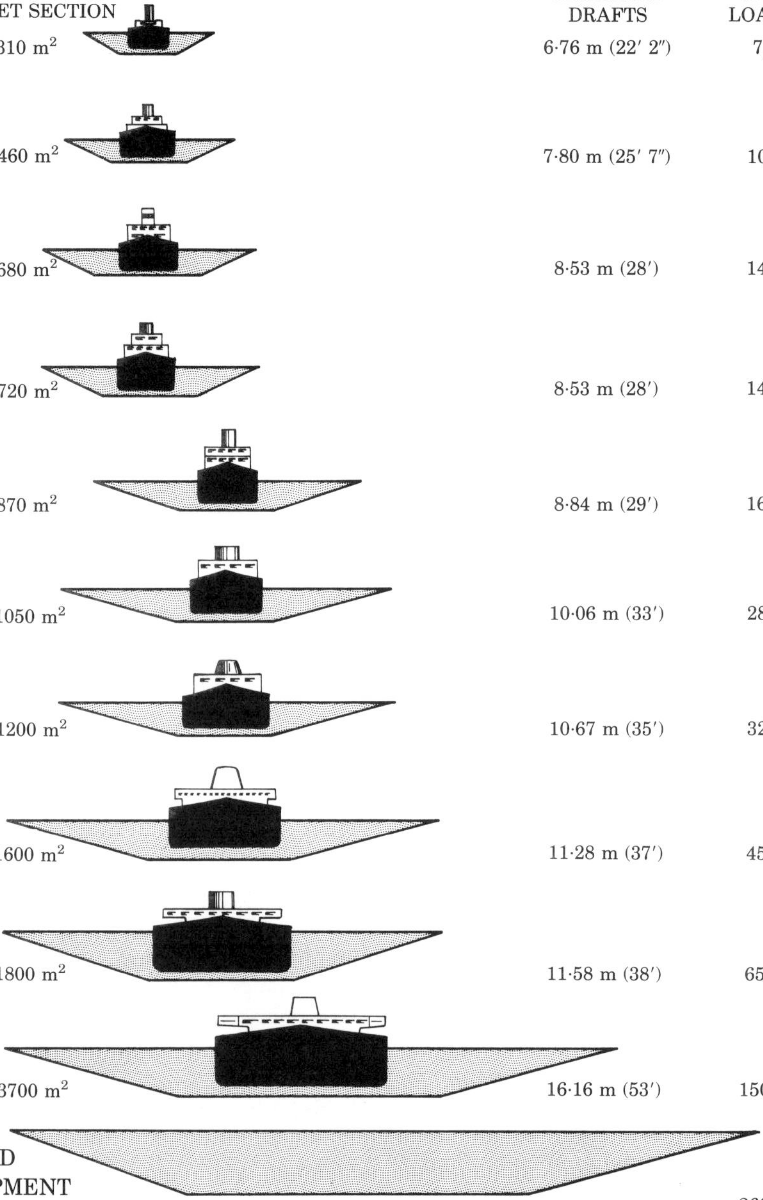

	WET SECTION	MAXIMUM DRAFTS	MAXIMUM LOADED SI
1869	310 m^2	6·76 m (22′ 2″)	7,000 dwt
1900	460 m^2	7·80 m (25′ 7″)	10,000 dw
1908	680 m^2	8·53 m (28′)	14,000 dw
1912	720 m^2	8·53 m (28′)	14,000 dw
1914	870 m^2	8·84 m (29′)	16,000 dw
1935	1050 m^2	10·06 m (33′)	28,000 dw
1954	1200 m^2	10·67 m (35′)	32,000 dw
1961	1600 m^2	11·28 m (37′)	45,000 dw
1964	1800 m^2	11·58 m (38′)	65,000 dwt
1980	3700 m^2	16·16 m (53′)	150,000 dw
PROPOSED DEVELOPMENT			260,000 dw

this massive growth in seaborne oil demand, in both absolute and relative terms, the world tanker fleet underwent a corresponding explosion, not only in size of tanker, but also in total carrying capacity. In 1938, the tanker fleet totalled just 17m DWT, by 1970 158m DWT and by 1930 325m DWT.

These post war years were the great ones for tankers. The crude oil carrier became the queen of the high seas. Not only did she grow to become twice as large as her nearest rival – the iron ore carrier – but the total tanker tonnage rose to account for some 50% of world merchant shipping by the '70s, including all bulk and general cargo shipping, passenger and fishing vessels, plus the thousands of small tugs, supply ships and miscellaneous craft. A truly staggering feat, deserving all the superlatives that could be thought up for it.

The British Petroleum South Pier at Mena al Ahmadi, Kuwait.

16 RAISING THE NEW FLAGS

One of the strangest facts about the tanker market is that it has remained so freely competitive. For some 60 uninterrupted years, the same powerful band of seven oil companies controlled international oil exports. Why did they not attempt to control the shipping of oil?

The answer probably lies in the fact that the tanker market has always been too open for the majors to try to control. Following the break-up of the Standard in 1911 by the US anti-trust legislation, the US majors have been very careful not to be seen forming cartels with their supposed competitors. Had they tried to manipulate the tanker market, there would always have been one independent shipowner prepared to scream "foul" from the roof tops. So any collusion between them had to be kept to those areas where it could be less easily seen – the more out-of-the-way oil markets of Africa, Australasia and the Far East.

As a result, the tanker market has stayed highly competetitive, free from the political and monopolistic manipulation that many so-called free markets have been forced to accept. Anyone has been free to buy a tanker and attempt to charter it. No licences, special rights by heritage, bribes or relatives in high places have been a prerequisite. Not even a special knowledge of oil has been necessary, just a team of operators, hopefully competent, but unfortunately not always, and a skilled broker. If the market was good, a quick fortune was to be made, if bad, rapid bankruptcy with nobody to bail one out.

This freedom has attracted many highly colourful and individual entrepreneurs into tankers over the years. The incredible growth in tanker demand after the Second World War created tremendous opportunities. New owners, new nationalities, new flags – as oil trades exploded, the strong could become giants overnight.

In the 19th century, Britain and her Empire dominated world trade and, not surprisingly, tanker ownership and registration. As the USA replaced her as the new superpower and oil trades developed around her coasts, US tanker ownership and US flag rose. After the Second World War, growth in demand turned to the Middle East, but this time ownership and flag did not follow suit.

The war itself was a major shock to the whole tanker world. Many vessels of all flags were destroyed, to be replaced by US-built tonnage. As in the First World War, only US yards were free from hostilities and so capable of replenishing the massive losses being sustained all round the European theatre of war. It was not until 1941, when the US government instigated the "emergency programme", that US shipbuilding became committed to help the allies. Between 1942 and 1945, 670 tankers were constructed, over 10m DWT in total – the world tanker fleet was only 17m DWT in 1938 and 23m in 1947.

When the war was over, the US Government found itself in exactly the same position as after the First – with a huge volume of surplus tonnage on its hands. Once again there were independent owners with cash at the ready from large insurance settlements from hulls lost during the war, and little shortage of demand for this good, cheap supply of second hand tankers. It was the US owners who benefited most. 447 T2 tankers were sold off by the US Maritime Commission; 244 went to US owners, nearly another 70 went under US control via the Panama flag and another 130 or so to European subsidiaries of the US majors via European flags.

In addition to the traumas of yet another war, the various crises in the Middle East during both the 1950s and '60s made the oil companies review their tanker ownership policies as well as refinery locations. Major trade routes to the west were openly vulnerable – Suez could be blocked or the pipelines to the Eastern Mediterranean cut by simply driving tractors into them. No wonder, therefore, the oil companies withdrew even further from ownership. An even greater slice of the tanker pie was to become available for the hungry independents, both new and old.

By the 1970s, the oil companies owned only some 35% of world tanker tonnage, compared with 54% in 1938 and nearly 90% in 1900.

The oil companies maintained a sufficient volume of tonnage to meet their long term requirements, without ever exposing themselves in times of crisis. As the potential repercussions of a single crisis became greater and greater, more tonnage was left to the independents. Even by 1970, the independent fleet was five times as great as the total world tanker fleet of 1938.

The law of the jungle and the free market are the same – the fittest survive, the weakest do not. To survive in shipping, an independent owner needs

Ownership of the world tanker fleet

	1938	*1960*	*1980*
Million DWT			
Oil companies	9	24	116
Independents	7	37	185
Governments	1	3	12
Others	—	—	12
Total	17	64	325
Breakdown			
Oil companies	54%	37%	35%
Independents	39%	58%	57%
Governments	7%	5%	4%
Others	—	—	4%
Total	100%	100%	100%

Source: *BP Statistical Review of World Energy*

to have a ship available at the right cost, at the right time and in the right place. It also helps if he himself is in the right place, where the big charterers are. After the War, there were three 'right' places if you wanted to get into tankers. Firstly, London – the oldest of all tanker markets and the centre of the non-US oil world. BP and Shell had their head offices here, plus most of the US majors with their eastern hemisphere control centres. Secondly, New York, the seat of final power for most of the US oil majors, and thirdly Tokyo, the natural focal point of the growing Japanese oil industry.

With the seven majors still controlling international oil, whether to Europe in the west or to Japan in the east, the right place had to be where they were.

The independent British owners in London, American in New York and Japanese in Tokyo were theoretically in the right place, but in practice were not always the fleetest of foot and often missed opportunities. Some of these openings in London and New York were picked up by the Norwegians, who had escaped from Norway during the war so they could run their ships for the good of the Allies and keep them out of German hands. However, the real stars of the post war boom were not the Norwegians but the Greeks.

The Greeks, like the Norwegians, had had the sea in their blood for thousands of years. And again, as in Norway, the sea was the natural means of communication; a mainland with a long tortuous coast line and much of the population living on small islands. For Greece, the sea was the only link to bind all the parts into one nation.

Greece was also in a unique location within the Mediterranean, midway between the eastern Mediterranean ports of the Lebanon, the southern European ports of France and Italy and the Black Sea ports of Russia. Just as

GROWTH OF THE WORLD TANKER FLEET BY FLAG

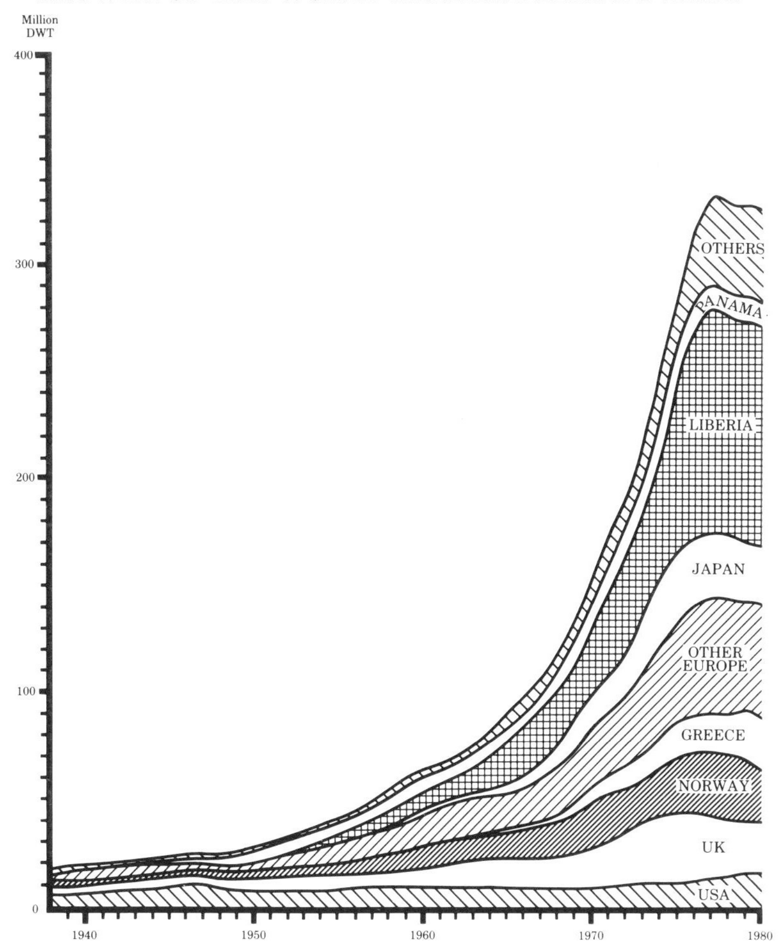

the Norwegians had relied on the North Sea timber as their staple cargo, so the Greeks did on the Russian grain from the Danube, through the Bosphorus and to Western Europe. The Mediterranean and the Black Sea were natural markets for the Greeks to tramp around looking for any type of dry cargo and also to be the ferrymen, and get people across these seas.

Not unnaturally, Greece became the major shipping nation in the Mediterranean. Most Greek islands and good ports on the mainland had their own shipyards and prided themselves in their own fleets, owned, managed and crewed by locals. Their ships were both dry cargo tramps and passenger vessels – generally of the smaller sizes suited for the calmer waters east of Gibraltar.

TANKER CHARTER RATES – 1947 to 1965

Dirty tankers fixed for single voyages for the Persian Gulf

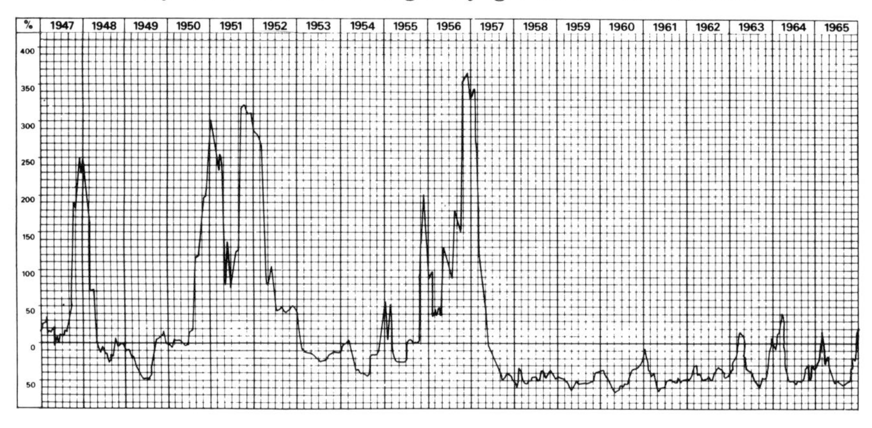

TANKER CHARTER RATES – 1966 to 1984

Dirty tankers fixed for single voyages ex the Persian Gulf

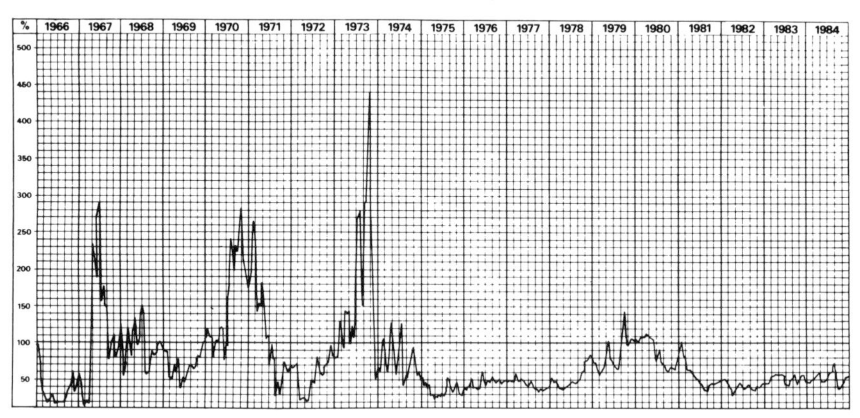

Sources: Conrad Boe Ltd. A/S Oslo
Lloyd's Shipping Economist

The big difference between Norway and Greece was the neighbours! Norway was on the edge of Europe, with peaceful countries around her for most years. Greece, on the other hand, was invaded by Turkey, surrounded by warring or quarrelling countries for centuries and so, unlike the Norwegians, Greeks often left home and went in search of quieter lands.

London, the maritime centre of the world, attracted many Greeks. The first London Greek shipping office was set up on 1886 and by the time the First World War was over, the Greek fleet had become roughly split into the London run ocean-going tonnage and the Mediterranean shipping run from Piraeus.

The Greeks had, of course, been involved in oil trades before the Russian revolution caused exports out of Batoum to dry up. At the turn of the century they were helping to ship Russian case oil in sailing ships. The first tanker under Greek flag was the *J. Koutsis*, built in 1902 and around 2,500 DWT. She was used in Russian exports as well and run from Piraeus by the Koutsi brothers.

It was not until the 1930s that a return of Greek interest in tankers was seen. The years between the wars were a period of great expansion of Greek shipping. Many cheap, war surplus vessels were bought, but most were dry cargo tramps rather than tankers.

This growth was not encouraged under the Greek flag. The then Prime Minister, General J. Mextaxas, saw the shipping community as a ready source of badly needed extra state revenue. When he tried to squeeze more money from those vessels still under Greek flag, owners immediately retreated and moved them to other flags.

The beginning of the modern Greek tanker fleet was not in London. Here the Greek shipping community was very much set in its traditional ways of dry cargo tramp shipping. It was the other side of the Atlantic that the big venture into tankers was to start.

As with many of the poorer nations of Europe at the turn of the century, the Greeks had crossed the Atlantic in droves in search of a bright new life in the New World. Three hundred thousand had emigrated to the USA in the decade before the First World War and the flow had become so great that the US Government had been forced to impose a quota of just 100 Greeks a year in 1921. The Greeks were, therefore, not just in London, but also very much in New York.

It was here that the first tentative involvment by the Greeks in the international tanker scene was to start. The two leading roles were taken by Onassis and Niarchos. Both were small time shipowners before the war and had begun in tankers during the '30s. After the war, many Greeks found themselves badly off as they had insured their ships through the Greek Insurance Fund. This did not have the funds to pay up all the war losses and the Greeks could not jump on the post war surplus tonnage boom. Only seven of the 447 war surplus US tankers were allocated to Greece. Neither Onassis nor Niarchos got one. They were spread around the more "traditional" US Greeks, not the "young upstarts". Niarchos was one of the lucky ones to get war damage compensation and got off to a flying start after the war with the settlement of a $2m claim. Onassis had lost none of his ships during the war and those that had not been blockaded in Europe had been making good profits. So he, too, started off after the war with cash in his hands.

Their tactics in buying tankers were very much like the Norwegians to begin with. They used "borrowed money", not cash and guaranteed their loans by five to 10 year charters from reputable oil companies. These methods were frowned upon by the traditional New York Greek shipping fraternity. The long-established Greek shipping families had always saved up for a new ship from profits out of their existing operations and never bought on credit.

Warnings against heavy borrowings fell on stony ground as far as these two were concerned. The logic of what they were doing was obvious to them, if not to their elders. Having long term charters from the majors was as good as "being backed by Rockefeller himself". For the majors, they could invest their money in projects which they viewed as being safer than tankers and allow them to expand their prime business – oil. For the Greeks it was almost a licence to print money.

It did not take Onassis and Niarchos long in their constant fight to beat each other to develop the Norwegian method of ship financing a stage further. Rather than ordering one tanker at a time, on the back of a single charter, they began to block book new tankers. They realised that by ordering a standard series of vessels at one yard, they could minimise the design costs and screw the yard down to a cost plus deal as they were offering guaranteed employment for not months, but years.

US yards quickly became full after the war. The obvious choice for this grand plan was Europe and where better than the war-torn, but highly efficient, yards of West Germany. With one flourish of a pen, they could create a construction programme for a yard, which would allow it to rebuild itself, its reputation and its future. With their rapidly growing armadas, they no longer had to restrict themselves to just long term guaranteed charters, but could spread their risks by leaving some of their vessels open to be played on the spot market. The booms in rates following Abadan and Suez during the '50s and the second Suez closure of 1967 only added further to their profits and their fleets.

By the mid-'60s, the Greek-controlled fleet was the largest single tanker fleet in the world. It had grown from virtually nothing in 1947 to 13m DWT by 1965 and 26m DWT by 1970. The Norwegian fleet had not stayed static. From 3m DWT in 1947, it had grown to 14m DWT in 1965, but to only 17m DWT by 1970.

The Greeks, being typical Mediterraneans, always preferred working with compatriots, preferably with their relations. Not only were Greek shipping communities quickly built up around any Greek shipowners, wherever these were in the world, but were all linked to the others into one big global family. There was great pride for a Greek in being in shipping and although the Greek tanker fleet might have seemed diffuse, in reality it was very much a national fleet and a very powerful force in the market. By 1970, it represented 17% of the world tanker fleet and 27% of the total independent fleet.

After the war, most Norwegians returned to Norway and ran their tankers under the Norwegian flag. Not so with the Greeks. Their homeland was still as insecure as ever and most preferred London, New York and (for Onassis) Monte Carlo, to Piraeus. For similar reasons, they also registered under other flags than the Greek. The Greek government took no positive steps to help them buy surplus war tonnage and the American banks were most unhappy to fund acquisitions under the Greek flag. Greeks were, therefore, forced to turn their backs on Greece and their national flag.

The US flag was no alternative to the budding Greek shipping magnates in New York. It was restricted to US owned, US built and US manned vessels and had already become prohibitively expensive for the US majors, let alone independents trying to fight for business in the open market. It was, therefore, to Flags of Convenience (FOCs) that they turned.

The first major tanker FOC was Panama. There have been FOCs for centuries. Owners have switched the flags of their vessels for the same old reasons of bypassing trade restrictions, avoiding taxes and ensuring that they would not be seized. The growth of FOCs in the 20th century was nothing new, it was just the magnitude of the exodus from the traditional flags that was different.

With hindsight the development of FOCs for tankers at this time was inevitable. Tight control over the US flag by both government and unions ensured that it was rapidly becoming uncompetitive on the open market. The US majors needed an alternative. The Greek flag was insecure, and the Greeks, too, needed a safe haven.

The Panamanian flag was first used as an FOC in 1922. Not by a Greek, but by an American and, amusingly, to ship a liquid cargo – not oil, but alcohol. It was prohibition which could be thanked. Back in 1906, the Anti-Saloon League had been founded to stop the sinful consumption of the vile poison. In 1919, it became illegal to manufacture, sell or transport alcohol in the USA except for medical purposes. And in 1922 when the United America Line was banned from selling or transporting alcoholic beverages aboard two of its cruise liners, the *SS Resolute* and the *SS Reliance*, the company switched them to Panamanian registry.

Panama was the ideal flag for such an action. The USA had helped her become independent from Columbia in 1903, although it had not been until 1914 that Columbia recognised this, and 1921 when the treaty had been at last ratified. The US involvement in Panama was considerable and was centred around the Panama Canal. Work had started on this in 1881, but had had to be halted in 1889 due to lack of finances. Another attempt was made in 1894, but stopped again in 1904. What was left of the company was bought up by the US Government with the coming of the new Republic of Panama, at the same time acquiring sovereign rights to the land either side – the Panama Canal Zone.

These ties gave US owners the security to register their ships under Panamanian flag without the fear of a sudden change of government and loss of control over them. Even Panama's maritime laws had been fashioned on those of the US. It was, therefore, not long after the United America Line's example that other US owners, in particular US oil companies, took to the Panamanian flag in an effort to reduce their crew costs.

By 1924, Lloyd's Register recorded 15 vessels under Panamanian flag. By 1936, there were 33 tankers under the flag and at the end of the war, in 1947, 89. Then came the big boom and in just one year the figure leaped to 173, or 1.4m DWT, some 10% of world tanker tonnage.

The Panamanian flag was useful to owners not only in peace but also during the war. Before the US had officially entered the war, the US could not use its own flag vessels to supply Europe. So by switching tonnage to the Panama flag, it could maintain its neutrality and the lifeline to the Allies in Europe.

In 1945, the US assisted in setting up another major FOC – not in the Americas but in Africa: Liberia. The US had had considerable involvement in Liberian rubber and iron ore and was able to persuade the Liberian authorities to lay down a maritime code offering similar freedom to the Panamanian flag. There were minimal restrictions on buying and selling, on the nationality of the owner and crew, where and how it operated and to what standard, plus cheap tonnage tax. Liberia and Panama were "convenient" in more ways than one.

The US authorities turned a blind eye to them. They wanted their nationals to own and control sufficient tonnage to supply the US in times of war, but were not prepared to upset the maritime unions by derestricting the US flag to allow low-paid foreigners to crew them. Better for US owners to put their ships under a friendly FOC and so remain internationally competitive, but also under "effective US control".

Following the war, US and Greek tankers began to flood into these two flags, especially Liberia. The move by US oil companies and independent owners alike into FOCs was such that soon they were being officially dubbed "Flags of Necessity" in the States and powerful lobbies were created to ensure their continued existence. By the early 1970s, the US-controlled fleet accounted for some 40% of Liberian and 65% of Panamanian tankers.

Under these two flags, the Greek tanker fleet prospered. The old ties with home were still very strong and seamen on board Greek ships were nearly always Greek and normally from the same village or island as that of the owner. The Greek government jealously watched the growth of this fleet. By 1964 the total Greek tanker fleet had topped 10m DWT, but less than 3m DWT was under Greek flag. By 1970, the fleet totalled 26m DWT and had become the largest in the world, pushing the British flag at 22m DWT into second place, whilst the Norwegian totalled only 17m DWT and the US some 9m DWT under the US flag, plus around 10m DWT "effectively controlled" under FOCs.

In 1953 and again in 1958, Greek governments attempted to woo Greek-controlled tonnage back to the Greek flag with beneficial tax privileges, but their success was very limited. By 1960 the Greek tanker flag fleet had actually topped 1m DWT. During the '60s only another 2m DWT was added, until yet another attempt was made in 1969, this time by the Colonels. This had a dramatic effect and by 1973, the year that the Colonels fell, there was over 10m DWT of tankers under the Greek flag. With the political stability that followed their fall from power, the fleet doubled to over 20m DWT during the rest of the '70s.

The FOCs up to the '70s were mostly the province of the US oil companies, US independents and the Greeks. The British flag was also used heavily by oil companies, plus British independents, and the Norwegian flags by Norwegian independents. It was tankers under these flags which principally served the massive trade routes to Western Europe, but flags for voyages to the other major oil importing region, Japan, were very different.

In order to guarantee a regular supply of crude oil after the war, the Japanese had been forced to accept the heavy involvement by US oil companies in their oil refineries. It was certainly not the normal practice of Japan to allow a foreign presence in a major sector of industry, but they had had little alternative as they needed oil and paid for it not just by giving a slice of their refining industry away but also in their purchase price of crude which, until the '70s, was always slightly higher than in the West.

This equity participation by foreign companies in the Japanese oil industry meant that they had control not only over a proportion of oil processing, distribution and marketing within Japan, but also over oil trades to Japan. In 1969, for example, 59% of Japanese refining capacity had some foreign involvement and this added up to 26% of total Japanese refining capacity. These foreign companies were inevitably the US majors and also Shell, plus Getty.

In practice they supplied nearly 100% of crude to Japan. It was only their equity share of refining processing that they could deliver themselves to Japan. The crude for their Japanese partners was sold by them ex the loading port and shipped by the Japanese. The foreign companies' element of Japanese tanker trades was covered in flags similar to those on western trades, but the Japanese sector was purely in Japanese flag bottoms.

In 1960, only 51% of all oil imported into Japan was in Japanese flag tonnage (55% for crude oil and 14% for refined products), whilst by 1970 the proportion had risen to 60% (64% for crude and 29% for products). The growth was a reflection of a lessening of the grip by the majors over Japan, as new refining capacity was built with no foreign involvement. However, the hand of the majors remained very much in evidence. Unlike in Western trades, the Japanese share was not covered in whole, or in part by oil company tonnage, but by independents (Japanese, of course) who centred around "the big six".

After the Suez crisis of 1956/57, there had been a recession in many areas of

Foreign involvement in Japanese refining (mid-1969)

Japanese refiner	*Refining capacity m.t.a.*	*Foreign share*	*Foreign capacity m.t.a.*	*Foreign company*
General Sekiyu Seisei	5.8	50%	2.9	Esso
Koa Oil	7.4	50%	3.7	Caltex
Kyokuto Oil	3.0	50%	1.5	Mobil
Mitsubishi Oil	10.2	48.7%	5.0	Getty
Nippon Pet. Ref.	17.1	50%	8.6	Caltex
Showa Oil	5.1	50%	2.5	Shell
Showa Yokkaichi Oil	9.0	25%	2.2	Shell
Toa Nenryo Kogyo	14.6	25%	3.7	Esso
		25%	3.7	Mobil
Maruzen Oil	8.6	20%	1.7	Shell
Total	80.8		35.5	
Japanese proportion of total	59%		26%	

world shipping. Too many vessels had been ordered on the back of the sudden boom in rates and, when the canal was reopened, a large surplus quickly developed and rates came crashing down. The Japanese merchant marine was particularly heavily hit. By the early 1960s, some 50 major shipping firms were in very serious financial difficulties. In 1963, therefore, the Japanese Government introduced new shipping industry "reconstruction" laws on which to rebuild a strong and profitable shipping community.

On the one hand, the new laws allowed a five-year period of grace for outstanding loan interest raised up to 1961, that is until profits were once again being made. On the other, those companies participating had to agree to amalgamate and submit their new construction plans for approval to the Ministry of Transport. The scheme was immediately successful and 80% of the whole Japanese merchant fleet applied for assistance. By 1967, 88 separate shipping companies had joined together under the six chosen nucleus shipping companies to create "the big six" – Kawasaki KK, Japan Line, Mitsui OSK, Nippon Yusen Kaisha, Showa Line and Yamashita-Shinnihon Steamship Co.

The reorganisation of the industry into a few powerful groups, plus central control over new construction via the annual "shipbuilding programme" gave the desired stability, reduced overcapacity whilst still allowing growth. Open competition was effectively eliminated as the six took the form of a cartel. Profits did return.

Not all major shipowners bowed to the strength of these government measures. One in particular, Sanko Line, decided to remain independent. In 1968, it returned the subsidies to the government rather than being locked into the official strait-jacket of the annual building programme. This stepping out of line was frowned upon by the rest of the big shipowners, but it was a clever and timely move. Sanko took great advantage of the booming world demand for tankers, being free now to build when ever it wanted to. By the early '70s, Sanko had overtaken all of the big six in oil carrying capacity except for Japan Line and NYK, and had a tanker fleet in excess of 4m dwt.

By the late '60s, Japanese owners began to find themselves being hit by exactly the same forces that had affected US owners 30 years earlier – high crew costs. Just as the Americans had been forced to look to FOCs, so now it was the turn of the Japanese. It was, however, not a simple matter of reflagging. The strong All Japan Seamen's Union was, not unnaturally, opposed to such moves and shipowners could not ignore its power. In addition, finance in Japan was getting tight as the rate of expansion of the Japanese fleet accelerated.

The Japanese, typically, found a unique solution. They either sold existing ships to foreign owners, but with "charter-back" arrangements, or they built new "tie-in" vessels, which they called "shikumisen", or "switching vessels". Tie-in tonnage was simply ships ordered by a foreign owner, built to the Japanese shipping company's specification, in Japanese yards, supervised during construction by this Japanese company and, like the charter-back vessels, operated under FOCs and chartered to the Japanese company. Via these circuitous routes, the Japanese could reflag their tankers without being threatened with action from the All Japan Seamen's Union, and at the same time gain access to cheap foreign finance.

The foreign shipping companies that the Japanese looked to for co-operation were – apart from a few deals with the Norwegians – a new breed of independent big ship owner, the Hong Kong Chinese. Just as the Europeans had been in the right place before the '60s, now it was the turn of the Chinese in the entrepreneurial centre of the Far East.

In Hong Kong, either British flag or FOCs could be used. Cheap Chinese crews were plentiful. The shipping expertise had come from mainland China when the Communists had come to power. By careful structuring of companies and revenue, no tax had to be paid and, once the Asian-dollar market really opened up in 1973, finance in the currency of international shipping – dollars – was readily available and at highly competitive rates. In New York, it had been the dollar and the Greeks – Onassis and Niarchos. Now in Hong Kong, it was the Asian dollar, Y. K. Pao and C. Y. Tung.

Both had left the mainland in the late '40s Y. K. Pao (later Sir Y. K.) had been a banker in Shanghai and bought his first ship in Hong Kong in 1955. He never lost his banker's instinct and prefered secure long term charters, keeping well out of the volatile spot market. C. Y. Tung had been involved in coastal shipping and he, too, prefered the long term charter market. What better for the Japanese, looking for foreign owners, to fit into long term charter-back and Shikumisen deals.

The need for this foreign Japanese-controlled tonnage was generated by the very barriers set up to protect the domestic market – the government reorganisation of the shipping industry. Like most attempts at bureaucratic control of a free market, it failed in part. The annual shipbuilding programme never completely covered the total domestic requirement for new tonnage and coupled with exchange controls, Japanese owners were forced to look abroad for their extra tonnage.

In the booming tanker market of the late '60s and early '70s, both Pao and Tung did incredibly well. Y. K. built up virtually all of his tanker fleet on the back of Japanese oil trades. It was only towards the end of the '70s that he moved into other areas of shipping and by the end of the decade, with a fleet of over 30m DWT, of which 15m was oil carrying tonnage, he had become the largest independent ship owner in the world. C. Y.Tung, on the other hand, served both the Japanese and the majors, once again with 15 to 20 year charters. By 1980, C. Y. had built up a tanker fleet of 9m DWT. Together these two owned 24m DWT, or 13% of the total independent tanker fleet. By comparison, Onassis owned only 6m DWT, Niarchos 3m DWT, and Norway's largest tanker owner, Sig Bergesen, 5m DWT.

So the era of the independent tanker owner was born. Vast fortunes were made by the successful. Not all made it; some went to the wall. The most notorious of all tanker owners to fall, when the good times eventually ceased, was Hilmar Reksten, from Bergen in Norway. He refused to follow the traditional strategy of having the bulk of his fleet on safe charters of at least three years and only a small proportion playing the spot market. He disliked anything but the spot market, which was fine when it was up. But all things that go up have to come down and the same is true of the tanker market.

Twice he was rescued from imminent bankruptcies, with the papers drawn up, both times by the closing of Suez – 1956 and 1967. However, when the market crashed in the mid-70s, Suez did not come to his rescue for a third time and his fleet of over 3m DWT of tankers was split between his sons after the Norwegian Government stepped in to save it. Reksten sadly died with a massive tax fraud case hanging over his head.

Reksten was not the only owner to suffer in the '70s. Too many Norwegians had become greedy in the boom following the 1967 Suez closure and, like Reksten, kept too many ships on the spot market. Fantastic profits were made and immediately pumped back into more and more new big ships. They all suffered harshly when the market crashed in late 1973.

Much tonnage had to be sold off during the late 1970s and early '80s, not just in Norway, but throughout northern Europe and moved to lower cost operations in the Far East. The Greeks were far more sensible than their colleagues to the north. They stuck to their old practices and, in general, kept out of the spot market, weathering the storm well. By the end of the '70s, the independent tanker fleet was scattered all over the globe, Hong Kong, Japan, Europe, America plus a host of other countries. No longer the exclusive province of the Northern Europeans, it was now truly international in very sense.

Daniel Keith Ludwig

Aristotle Onassis

Stavros Niarchos

Minos Coloctronis

Giants of the 1970s tanker trades: C. Y. Tung, Sir Y. K. Pao.

17 THE MASS MEDIUM

The tanker market may be slave of the oil market, but it is the master of the shipbuilders. It wanted ships by the hundreds and got them. But not by the old one-off, hand-tailored methods used before the war. The name of the game now was mass production.

It was the war itself which created the demand for masses of instant ships – the Allies lost 4,786 vessels of all kinds during the six years of hostilities from 1939 to 1945. By adapting the assembly line techniques of the Detroit car industry to shipbuilding, the Americans revolutionised ship construction. The key was "the standard design".

Pre-war, the owner told the builder what he wanted. Now it was the yard which said what was available. The standard design met the typical requirements of the market, and most important of all, it could be readily repeated. This meant that each section of the ship, each large piece of machinery, each pipe and each valve had to be planned in advance, had to be capable of being built *en masse,* available at the critical time and assembled in the shortest period into a complete ship. Frills and one-off modifications had to be kept to a minimum, and during the war, excluded.

The job of running the American war-time construction programme was in the hands of the US Maritime Commission. This organisation had been established under the 1936 Merchant Marine Act in an attempt to revitalise US shipping and shipbuilding in the depths of the Great Depression. It built very few vessels until suddenly in January 1941 the "Emergency Programme" was thrown at it. The first order was for 260 ships! Under huge pressure to create masses of tonnage over night, it had to look to standard designs.

Various designs were created, but the two most famous were the dry cargo "Liberty" ships – 2,709 were built during the war – and the "T2" tanker. Six hundred and eighty-four T class tankers were built, of which 481 were the legendary T2-SE-A1 series – 16,613 DWT, 503′ LOA, 30′ 1¼″ draft and a 6,000 HP turbo electric engine giving them 14½ to 15 knots and crewed by 44 seamen.

US Maritime Commission T class construction programme (1939-45)

	'39	*'40*	*'41*	*'42*	*'43*	*'44*	*'45*	*Total*	*Post-war*
No. of Tankers	7	5	2	33	175	266	196	684	5 built 1946 81 cancelled

Source: *Victory Ships & Tankers by L. A. Sawyer and W. H. Mitchell*

The T2s were magnificent ships and lasted well into the 1960s as a class of their own. Even after 35 years, a number are still trading, admittedly after rebuilds.

Up to this time, ships had been built in one piece – from keel up – and on slipways. Output of yards was, therefore, directly related to the number of slips and the average time of construction. The new method was to prefabricate large sections on special land sites near the building berth, whilst another hull was being assembled on the berth. Then as soon as this was launched, the various completed sections of the next ship could be rapidly assembled on the berth. Again, as soon as she was finished, she would be launched to be fitted out at a nearby quay, leaving room for the next to be put together. Output was now limited by the logistics of simultaneous fabrication.

What was good for the war was good enough for peace and US yards continued to develop their new mass production techniques after the war. One might have expected European yards to retool immediately in the face of such competition and follow suit, but no. The resistance to change was too strong in many European yards, particularly British, and they stuck with their old outmoded technology.

In defence of the old European yards, it must be said that they were in a state of shock after the war and desperately short of cash. Their ability to redesign their whole production methodology was limited, but even so there was remarkedly little enthusiasm from the Europeans for this supposed new fangled and typically American slapdash way of throwing ships together.

US labour costs were by this time far in excess of those in Europe. This extra boost to American productivity succeeded in allowing US yards to maintain their competitive edge over the Europeans in the immediate post-war period. US yards soon filled up with new orders. The Europeans gained nothing but a false sense of security as they enjoyed the overspill which could not be taken up on the other side of the Atlantic.

The European failure to recognise the threat of mass production in shipbuilding was a grave error. They were right in concluding that there was little to fear from affluent America, but they forgot about Japan. Unlike the USA, Japanese labour was not high cost. Even more important neither was the Yen – fixed at Y360 to the US dollar in April 1949. The combination of cheap labour costs, a low exchange rate and high US mass production productivity was world beating.

Almost miraculously, the Japanese shipbuilding industry had come through the war virtually unscathed. However, there was no work for their yards as the Allied Occupation Forces severely restricted any attempts at the Japanese building of deepsea ships. It was not until the Korean war broke out in 1950 that these constraints were removed. For two years America scrambled to keep her armed forces in the Far East supplied with gasoline. The tanker market moved into a healthy boom, but the Japanese gained few orders. What they did win was their freedom to build again for whomsoever they liked. All they needed was the technical knowhow and this came in the form of the Texas oil magnate Daniel K. Ludwig.

Back in 1936, Ludwig had entered tanker ownership by forming National Bulk Carriers (NBC), which during the next 30 years was to be a world leader in building many of the largest tankers afloat. Early in the war, he had diversified into shipbuilding and constructed some of the T3 class tankers at his Welding Shipyard in Norfolk, Virginia on the US East Coast, but this facility was limited to 30,000 DWT and not what Ludwig wanted after the war.

He wanted a yard that could build mammoths and he turned to Japan. What could have been better than the Imperial Japanese Naval Dockyard at Kure, with both its 150,000 DWT dock and shops unharmed by the war. In 1951 he therefore took out a 10 year lease on Kure and introduced mass production. For the rest of the decade, NBC built the largest tankers in Japan. In 1952 the 38,000 DWT *Petro Kure*, 1954 the 45,000 DWT *Phoenix*, 1955 the *Sinclair Petro-Lore* at 55,000 DWT, 1956 the 85,500 DWT *Universe Leader*, and in 1959 the 103,000 DWT *Universe Apollo*.

Other Japanese shipbuilders were fascinated at what was happening at Kure and soon followed in Ludwig's footsteps. The Abadan and Suez crisis all helped to maintain pressure on demand for new tankers. Traditional owners from Europe and America were eager to order on the back of this boom and found that Japanese price, quality and delivery dates were all good – the Japanese economic miracle had hit tankers.

Old slipways were quickly phased out and all-purpose built assembly line dry docks with huge fabrication shops brought in. The man hour per ton of shipping constructed in Japan was slashed; in the six years between 1958 and 1964 it came down by 60%. Whole yards were designed around the central theme of mass producing massive tankers. New standard designs were created to make

RANGE OF DEEPSEA TANKER SIZES BY DELIVERY DATE

construction easier and hence quicker and hence cheaper. Marketing teams went out to sell as many of each standard design as possible so as to minimise development costs. Massive gantry cranes became the norm, to tower over shipbuilding towns and allow prefabricated 200 ton chunks of tankers to be shuffled around the yard like dice. By the mid '60s, new docks were more elongated so that a whole 200,000-tonner plus the stern, and hence main machinery, of the next ship could be put together simultaneously. By the '70s, computers designed the ships and cut steel plates to exact shapes, a very far cry from the industry 50 years before.

In Europe, many yards turned a blind eye to what was happening in the Far East. Consequently in the '60s, they found that they had slipped hopelessly behind Japanese technology, productivity and, most important, price. Their hardware was outmoded and their management techniques archaic. They had to face the alternatives of either scrapping their existing plant and rebuilding from scratch, or just going bust. Many failed to make the vital decision in time and have never caught up. Others forced through painful reorganisations and have survived, but not unscathed.

In the face of Japan Incorporated, it was only those with the greatest flexibility of management and manpower, or those with the most generous government coffers who lived through into the 1980s. The traditional shipbuilding nations of Europe could not believe that their heritage and "right" was being won away by these Far Eastern upstarts. But such was the ferocious expansion of Japanese shipbuilding capacity, that by the early '70s Japan was accounting for just under half of total world merchant tonnage launched and her output was vastly greater than any other single nation in the whole world – some eight times as large as West Germany and Sweden, 10 times as large as the UK, France and Spain, 20 times greater than the USA. Today, most European and American yards can only compete internationally through massive government support.

The war brought not only assembly lines, but also renewed welding. This technique had been in use before the war in shipbuilding, but was neither totally safe nor suitable for extensive use. In general, welded hulls for tankers were viewed with considerable suspicion. The war gave the necessary impetus to improve both techniques and materials and by the end of the hostilities all-welded ships had proved themselves.

Welding allowed hulls to be made lighter and stronger. They could also be put together much quicker so welding was an essential element in the concept of mass production. As steel quality was continually improved, even lighter hulls could be tolerated. For example, the introduction of high tensile steel in the early '70s made a major contribution to the ability of the industry to build tankers over a quarter of a million tons deadweight.

Welding was the key to automated ship construction – the first all-welded Japanese tanker was launched in 1948. As the assembly line technique developed, so did the production line and remote controlled welding – again with the Japanese in the lead. After huge steel plates had been automatically cut to precise shapes by computer controlled cutting torches, multi-headed automatic welding machines joined the various strengthening and angle pieces on to individual plates in purpose-built welding shops. All that was left to do by hand was to weld up these sections and then join all the prefabricated blocks together in the dock.

The constant demand for more and more tankers saw both the overall size of the fleet and the individual range of ships' sizes increase. By the early '70s, the deepsea tanker fleet consisted of the whole spectrum of vessels from 15,000 to 500,000 DWT.

This was the ideal for the market. The latest record-breaking size of super tanker could be designed and used on the longest runs, from the ever expanding fields of the Persian Gulf, allowing the smaller and older vessels to be pensioned off on the shorter trades from Africa to Europe, or from Indonesia to Japan. By the '70s, therefore, the Gulf regularly handled 250,000-tonners and above, West Africa 120/250,000 DWT vessels and North Africa, plus crude loading terminals in the Far East for 50/120,000-tonners.

Most shipbuilders had only to concern themselves with designing tankers for Persian Gulf crude. This simplified their lives considerably. Crude oil qualities from parts of the world or even fields in the same region can be very different, necessitating alternative design criteria. For instance, different specific gravities need different optimum tank configurations, whilst different viscosities need different valves and pumps, and even the installation of heating coils.

There were just three dominant Persian Gulf grades of crude oil – Saudi Arabian Light, Iranian Light and Kuwait. All three were of very similar quality, coming from the same family of crudes. Although there were slight variations between them, these were small enough for the shipbuilder to consider them, and hence all Persian Gulf crude, as just one single grade. For some 30 years after the war, therefore, the shipbuilding industry was in the wonderful position of only having to worry about designing new tankers for one grade of cargo.

The crude oil tanker became a standard design in more ways than one. The products tanker, on the other hand, often still had to be individually designed to a particular trade and range of likely cargo parameters. The crude oil tanker design could be readily pulled off the shelf and adapted to whatever new monster size was in fashion. Such simplicity had obvious advantages for new yards. Evolving shipbuilding nations in the third world, such as South Korea and Brazil, eagerly jumped on the supertanker band waggon, offering even cheaper prices than the Japanese and doing even more harm to the traditional yards of Europe and America.

Competition to open new mammoth shipyards became frenetic towards the early '70s. Many underdeveloped countries saw shipbuilding as the ideal way of starting up an industrial export base. Government funds were often used to subsidise the development of these green field yards. No wonder European and American yards could not compete without similar government assistance.

In the face of this growing Third World competition, the Japanese still managed to maintain their lead through these years, not just through high productivity and keen prices, but also through their ability to design the largest of engines. The key element in building the largest of tankers had no longer become the size of the dock, but the power output of the main propulsion unit. With the cost of the main engine accounting for some 20/25% of the total capital cost of a supertanker, the typical independent owner could not afford to install twin power units in order to generate the necessary propulsion output for even bigger hull designs – it was only the major oil companies who could afford such luxuries. Developments in hull size, therefore, followed from developments in engine design.

As demands for more powerful engines grew, builders switched their favours from motor to steam turbine units. Above 100,000 DWT, the norm became steam, between 25,000 and 100,000 DWT either steam or motor, whilst under 25,000 DWT generally motor. Japanese engine builders concentrated on steam turbine and led the world with the biggest and most efficient, so keeping ahead of any fledgling shipbuilding nation's technology.

The effect of oil refining capacity shifting from source to market locations was very marked on the crude tanker and its size. It also radically changed the demand for the products tanker, where two very different roles developed for it.

One was similar to its traditional job – "distributive" trading – delivering small parcels of oil from the refiner to the final consumer, but the other – "balancing" trading – was new. This necessitated levelling out the imbalances in particular product streams between different refining areas around the world. So, unlike distributive trades, which tended to be short coastal trades, these were long deepsea voyages.

The important distributive trades developed around the coasts of North West Europe, the Caribbean islands and the Far East where many consumers were located near to the sea. US coastal trades were still closed to any flag other than the US through the Jones Act, as were Japanese coastal movements to Japanese flag by similar laws and of no interest to the international shipowner.

The workhorse of the international products tanker market was the 18,000-tonner, known by everyone as the "handy-size". By the early '70s it had developed into 25/30,000 DWT through the sheer increase in trade volume. Much of this distributive trade could be channelled via large deep water ports, but not all, and it was the multitude of low volume ports which could not be economically developed that put the major constraint on the design of the handy sized tanker. Often it was the length of the berth which remained critical. Draft could be increased as long as the ship called at the deeper ports first and as DWT increased, draft and beam grew but length stayed at 560 feet.

To cater for the growing number of product grades, these ships were built to very specific designs and could carry up to 20 different grades at one time. Normally independent owners did not build these expensive vessels on spec, but only for guaranteed long term employment to a particular oil company and often to the oil company's own design. This sector of the market, therefore, tended to be covered by the oil companies themselves; the spot charter market would not always pay the premium needed to cover the sophistication of one of these vessels. Independent owners who foolishly built them without the necessary long term cover found them very costly mistakes when the market collapsed in the '70s.

The big balancing trades, such as between the Mediterranean and North West European refineries, or North American and between the Middle Eastern and Far Eastern, were ideal for the ageing, smaller crude carrier. Generally only one grade of product had to be shipped and in big parcel sizes, so anything up to 70,000 or even at times 100,000 DWT crude tankers could be pensioned off into these relatively undemanding trades. The better hulls could cope with clean products, whilst those nearing the ends of their lives with leaky bulkheads could potter around in dirty products.

One of the biggest products trades was, and still is, from the Caribbean refineries to the US East Coast. As well as plants on Aruba and Curacao, others were added on Trinidad, St Croix and the Bahamas. The US quota system of 1959 restricted crude and distillate imports, but not residues. There was, therefore, a large demand for cheap foreign fuel oils and the nearest refineries not on American soil (but for the most part in American ownership) were in the Caribbean. And into this unsophisticated, high volume, dirty products trade were attracted all the old rust buckets from the four corners of the globe.

It was incredible that some managed to deliver oil into the States at all, they leaked so badly. No wonder the citizens along the US East Coast south of New York became some of the most paranoid environmentalists in the world with their beautiful beaches continually being fouled by badly run and badly maintained old tankers. But it was not just the tankers which were to blame. These post war years saw not only a boom in oil trades, but also other bulk cargoes such as iron ore, coal and grain.

Iron and coal for steelmaking underwent a similar, but not quite as large boom as oil, especially to Japan who had neither commodity domestically and had to import both. Specialist ore and versatile dry bulk carriers evolved, whilst on some routes oil could be combined in one direction with dry bulk in the other leading to combined oil/ore carriers, or O/Os, in the '50s and ore/bulk/oil or OBOs, and bulk/ore/ or B/Os in the 60s.

One of these combined trades was from Hampton Roads on the US East Coast to Japan with coal, via the Panama Canal, returning west bound to the Middle East to pick up oil for the US East Coast ports such as New York and Philadelphia. If having discharged its oil, the ship had to return to Hampton Roads there was little time to clean out its tanks at sea. Theoretically it should have sailed some miles off shore, carefully cleaned itself, preferably retaining the washings onboard for discharge into land tanks at Hampton Roads. In practice many masters took the shortest route, sailing close to the shore, and dumped any tank washings straight overboard. How the East Coast beaches suffered.

The combination of oil and other cargoes went back to the 19th century, of course. In those days specialised combined carriers were not necessary. Tankers could be cleaned for dry cargo, at cost, and in the Far East regularly traded in both wet and dry. A similar phenomenon was also to occur in the late '50s while the specialised combined carrier was still a rarity. This special dual wet and dry trade for pure tankers still persists today, but only in small volumes.

Under US Public Law 480, surplus US grain could be shipped to the needy nations of the Third World and paid in local currencies rather than US dollars. India and other Asian countries were badly short of food and there was a constant trade of US grain to the east. Unfortunately, the Suez crisis of 1956 created a severe shortage of dry cargo tonnage and the Indian Supply Mission turned to a combination of Middle East oil to the USA plus US grain from the Gulf Coast to India in tankers as the most economic solution.

The ships tanks had to be chemically cleaned, deodorised and freed of all traces of oil after each oil cargo. This technique was soon perfected and cost between $12,000 for a 20,000-tonner and $17,000 for a 30,000-tonner in the late '60s. Owners were initially concerned that the grain cargoes might increase their maintenance costs, but this fear proved unfounded. All pipework had to be closed off and discharge and loading pipes in the cargo tanks boxed in wood. Grain could be simply loaded via the small deck tank hatches and equally easily sucked out by vacuum machines. The dynamic movement of the grain was very similar to that of a liquid and so tankers handled well with this alien cargo onboard.

Tankers in grain became a regular feature of the market in the 1960s, especially when tanker rates were depressed and dry cargo firm. However this area of the market never became more than marginal, accounting for perhaps only some 1% to 2% of total tanker employment at any time and limited to the smaller sizes due to port limitations at both ends of the trade. Much of the tonnage was US flag. These US government aid deals with the Third World, plus bilateral grain sales to Russia automatically secured a high percentage of the grain exports for US flag vessels. Since the US did not, and for that matter still does not, have more than a handful of national flag dry bulk carriers, US flag tankers had to be used and if they were not available then the US chartered in open flag tonnage.

For the shipbuilding industry, these years after the Second World War were some of the most challenging it had ever encountered. There was constant demand for more, bigger and efficient ships. Competition to win orders was cut throat and so considerable sums of money had to be ploughed back into research and development for yards to keep ahead of their competitors. Most of the new technical breakthroughs came out of Western Europe and Japan, either from individual yards and their suppliers, or national research organisations.

The old war built T2s had had a turbo-electric main engine, but this was not suitable for the new larger breeds of tankers. Experiments were made with gas turbines and even nuclear was talked about in the early '70s. In the end, it was only the diesel and steam turbine designs which stood the test of time. These continued to find favour with owners, not only because they could be developed to power ever larger hulls, but also because they remained efficient.

Although voyage lengths increased considerably, speeds did not. Oil remained a low value cargo and there was no necessity to have a lot faster ships to carry it. Design speeds increased from around 14 knots after the war to some 16 to 16½ knots by the '70s. But even if there was no significant increase in the carrying efficiency of the fleet, there were tremendous strides made in improving hull efficiency.

Welding reduced hull drag as the outside of the tanker was now flat with no overlapping plates and protruding rivets. In the early 1960s the bulbous bow was introduced with reported gains in speed of ½ knot: this new bow design set up a wave which counter balanced and so eliminated most of the normal bow wave and reduced power requirements. In the late '60s and throughout the '70s, considerable advances were made in external hull paints. Special toxic paints were developed which severely retarded the growth of weed and barnacles, allowing the vessel to maintain her maximum speed at minimum power for far longer periods of time. Fuel consumption was, therefore, conserved and dry docking intervals increased from a year to over two years and in exceptional cases, five years.

Technical advances were made inside the hull too. Automation steadily reduced the number of crew from 50 or over to under 30 in some instances. However, the strengthening of maritime unions around the world counteracted this trend, forcing owners to improve pay and conditions in return for demanning agreements. For those fleets operating under the national flags of Western Europe and Japan where union power was strong, there was a great incentive to move to larger tankers. Bigger ships meant that crew costs represented a smaller proportion of the unit cost of transporting oil and so these economies of scale could be used to offset the diseconomies of maritime unions. For those owners under FOCs, their cost advantage versus the old traditional tanker flags just grew greater.

Improved conditions for the seamen meant amongst other things more regular hours and less unpleasant work. On-voyage maintenance by the crew came to be a thing of the past under many national flags, to be replaced by flying squads to handle certain types of repairs and maintenance work. In the '60s, the old physical division of officers and crew by the three island design also disappeared. All accommodation was moved aft into one massive tower block to create the new social unit with fitted carpets, swimming pools, TVs in every cabin and even room for wives to go to sea.

It may sound as though life at sea had become one of luxury, but thanks to the supertanker this was far from the real world. Gone were the regular calls at welcoming ports around the world. Now life was simply a steady shuttle to and fro between offshore terminals in the Persian Gulf and Western Europe or the Far East. Thanks to the designers of pumping systems, a 300,000-tonner could still turn around in the two days that a 15,000-tonner took at either load or discharge port. So on Europe run from the Gulf around the Cape, the crew only had four days out of a total round voyage time of 68 days at a terminal and as often as not this was stuck miles out at sea.

Crews on products tankers lived a far more civilised life than those on the big crude carriers. At least they only went on short voyages, with many port callings on their milk runs, feeding all their multitude of customers with different grades of refined oil. To help them get in and out of all the berths, channels and ports safely, special equipment was fitted. Small propellers, called bow thrusters, were installed at right angles to the length of the ship in the bows, giving them much greater manoeuvrability. Special ballasting and deballasting arrangements were designed allowing them to drop a bit of this grade off here and a bit of that there. Sophisticated tank coatings were developed to minimise corrosion, tank cleaning time and money and to maximise segregation flexibility.

Although the hulls of tankers may have seemed rather like sausages coming out of a sausage machine, what went into and onto them certainly was not. The problem was always how to make the total unit more efficient and since it was run by men, the man/machine interface became a new problem that the industry had to face. With more leisure time and more money there was a greater opportunity for the seaman to become unhappy at sea. This could affect both his and his shipmate's work and so a new breed of marine life appeared, the industrial sociologist.

The steel shell built around the old Isherwood design was now crammed with high technology kit – automated engine rooms, computer styled collison avoidance radars, satellite communication links to head offices, automatic stress sensors around the hull. But all this was manned by fewer and fewer crew and had to be sailed on seas filled with more and more vessels of greater size and less manoeuvrability.

As soon as the first supertanker was talked about, environmentalists jumped on their soap boxes and ranted and raved about the inevitable catastrophe where one of these monsters would go aground, spilling its cargo of death and destruction to all living matter that it came in contact with. The oil industry skilfully rejected this, using its smooth public relations machine.

"The bigger that tankers are, the fewer that there would be on the high seas" the oil companies argued, "and so the less the risks of a major accident." You can do anything with statistics so they say, and it was not surprising that their opponents turned the argument round and said that "you only need one supertanker for a major disaster. The bigger they are the bigger the likely disaster."

In the end, neither proved to be right for it was neither the number, nor the size that really mattered, but the quality of men on board. On March 16, 1978 a 240,000-tonner owned by Amoco, one of offsprings of the old Rockefeller Standard Oil of Indiana, had steering failure off the cost of northern France. The master of the *Amoco Cadiz* refused the assistance of a deepsea tug that had heard of his plight and come to his rescue. The tug master demanded a Lloyd's Open Form, which meant that he would have total salvage rights over the ship. The master of the VLCC contacted his head office in Chicago for instructions and as the argument raged across the Atlantic the worsening weather was blowing the ship towards the rocks. Eventually the master of the *Amoco Cadiz* agreed to let the tug put a line on and hence agree Lloyd's Open Form, but by this time it was too late. The weather had deteriorated and she was too near the shore. The tow broke and she went aground with a full cargo of Iranian crude.

The next day she broke her back and spilled a quarter of her 223,000 tons of oil. The French Government immediately decreed a national disaster and called in the troops. They could do little but try to mop up. Over 100 miles of beautiful and wide coastline was covered in a deadly slick of oil. The death toll of wild life was so great it could not be counted. On the 28th the forepeak broke in two, spilling the rest of her cargo and the French sent in the airforce and depth charged her. In June the cost was estimated as being $75m, of which the French army accounted for $12.5m, by November it had escalated to $110m, excluding the value of the ship and cargo. By 1982, $2 billions worth of writs had been filed against Amoco in the States including those of some 90 French towns and villages.

Under international law Amoco was only directly responsible for a few million pounds, although it could cost in total some $10m to resolve the US law suits. But these were not the only costs to Amoco. So bad was the public outcry that the company's petrol sales were reported to have dropped by some 15% and stayed down for two to three years. The other oil companies watched with horror as Amoco's image was dragged through court after court and down every front page in Europe. One tanker was not worth that loss of image which had taken millions of dollars and decades to build up. So, unlike the independents who were slashing costs left right and centre with the market in the worst of depressions, the oil companies quietly kept up maintenance and put the best equipment onboard, praying that they would never have an *Amoco Cadiz*.

This was far from being the only VLCC accident, but it was certainly the worst. The era of supertankers and mass production also brought the biggest mass explosions. In the late '60s and early '70s, there was a spate of mysterious VLCC explosions. Most happened in ballast conditions and when the ships were tank cleaning at sea. Whole decks of ships, a quarter of a mile long, were ripped off as though a giant tin opener had attacked them. Some sank without trace.

Even today the answer to this is not clear. It is thought that the main reason may be that sub-atmospheres can be created inside the huge tanks of these ships. Under certain regular and heavy wave conditions, ballast water can slop around and set up an electrostatic cloud inside the tank, just like a miniature thunder cloud which can discharge, and bang. Who said big is beautiful?

In order to protect both crew and ship, the industry came up with IGS, Inert Gas System. IGS simply diverts flue gas from the stack into the cargo tanks. It is pumped in to maintain a constant positive pressure relative to the outside atmosphere and so form a safe, inert blanket over either the cargo, or ballast. Unfortunately it was prone to going wrong if not carefully maintained, as well as giving a false sense of security to the crew. More than one tanker exploded with its IGS system supposedly operational.

Tankers were still dangerous and still had the potential for massive pollution of the seas. Gradually the international community got its act together and IMCO (nowadays IMO), the United Nations Maritime body, got agreement from the maritime nations of the world for new rules and regulations on tanker safety, but the world had to wait until the early '80s for them to be ratified and imposed. Depending upon the type, size and year of build of tanker, owners were now forced to introduce IGS, COW or SBT. All systems had been around for years, but only the reputable owners like the majors, the Scandinavians and a few odd owners scattered around the globe had already installed them.

COW, or crude oil washing was an ingenious tune played by BP on the old Butterworth tank cleaning system. Rather than pumping water, one recycled part of the crude cargo. This got rid of the oily deposits from the tank walls and reduced sludge and slops dramatically. SBT, or segregated ballast tanks was very much what it says, for special tanks were kept for ballast water, ensuring that cargo and ballast were never carried in the same tank.

Will IMO regulations make tankers safe and clean? We will have to wait to see, for as with the *Amoco Cadiz*, it is men who cause disasters, not machines. The 20-odd years after the Second World War both created the super monster and were the golden years for the tanker industry. Technology had given birth to the biggest ships ever seen on the high seas, just as the demand for oil had pumped the tanker fleet up to be the "biggest and bestest" type on earth. The trouble is that what goes up can always come down. Someone was always going to prick the bubble.

The broken *Amoco Cadiz,* offshore, Brittany. A tanker disaster which affected 200kms of French holiday coast and caused major problems for the French authorities.

18 ENERGYQUAKE – THE BIG SLUMP

There seemed to be an infallible logic in the post-war years as demand for oil and tankers kept on expanding from year to year. Oil, everyone said, was the ultimate energy source. It would continue to capture markets from coal and its demand would continue to grow at the ever increasing rate it had done since the Second World War. What went for oil also went for tankers. The question was not whether the million-tonner would ever be built, but when.

How wrong everyone was. Rather than watching the tanker market go from strength to strength, owners saw it go into a slump to end all slumps, the deepest recession of all its 100 odd years of existence. In September 1973 the market was at the height of its biggest boom – by December the slide had started and took nearly a year to hit rock bottom.

To begin with few took it really seriously. They expected the depression to last only three, or at the most five years. By 1978, it was obvious to all that this was no ordinary slump for there was still a 30–40% oversupply of tanker capacity. By 1982, rather than getting better, it had got far worse; 60–70% of the fleet was surplus to demand. A different perspective was now put on 1973, no longer was it viewed as just another boom, but the ultimate boom, a glorious height from which the market could only decline.

The reason for this collapse stemmed, of course, from oil, and was by no means a sudden turn of events. The seeds of destruction had been sown many years earlier, but no one had bothered to notice them when they began to surface in the late '60s. In the early '70s when they had grown large enough for all to see, still they were ignored: everyone was having far too good a time making money.

It is very easy to be wise after the event. The reasons for what happened seem crystal clear today, but back in 1970 it was equally easy to misinterpret the signs. However, it is surprising that neither the oil nor the tanker worlds showed any caution when OPEC began to flex its muscles with the first tentative, but unilateral price rises in 1970. When the boom of 1970 was followed by an even bigger one in 1973, both industries survived massive volumes of new capacity. With the collapse later that year, the resulting world surplus of refinery and tanker capacity was staggering and it was by no means just the tanker market which was to be hit for many years to come.

So what really happened to cause this catastrophe? We all know that OPEC forced up the price of oil by quantum leaps in 1973 and 1979, causing world economic recessions. Not only was the demand for oil cut back, but energy consumers looked for any way to conserve and so reduce consumption further, plus whether to switch into cheaper alternatives to oil. Although OPEC controlled both world oil and gas prices, coal was free from its power. Over night, the tables were turned and from being an expensive energy source, coal became cheap. Markets that had been lost to oil for decades were suddenly won back and oil demand became even more depressed. But these are the effects, not the causes. Why, therefore, did OPEC push up the price of oil from just over $1 a barrel in 1969 to over $30 a barrel in 1979?

To answer this we have to go back to 1959, the year that the USA brought in its oil import quotas. This action by the US Government created two things:

1) a surplus of oil outside the USA, and therefore downward pressure on world prices throughout the '60s;
2) OPEC itself in 1960 in an oil producers' attempt to maintain and improve oil revenues and world prices.

There can only be one price for a commodity and these two forces were incompatible. During the '60s, the majors still controlled world oil and OPEC could do nothing about either high output or low prices, but in 1970 this control shifted. The pent-up frustration of the past decade burst through with the savage price increases.

In 1960, OPEC had managed to get posted prices frozen. Although open market prices continued to fall during the '60s, posted prices stayed fixed. By 1969, therefore, Arabian Light could be bought at $1.20 a barrel, whereas its posted price was still at the 1960 value of $1.80 a barrel. In real terms, although the posted price had dropped considerably in value, it should have risen to $2.50 to $3.00 a barrel by 1969 to have kept in line with inflation – a fact that had not escaped the attention of OPEC.

Throughout the '60s OPEC was extremely active trying to get posted prices raised, even if just to keep them in line with inflation. Individual members constantly asked the majors for increases, always to be fobbed off with some

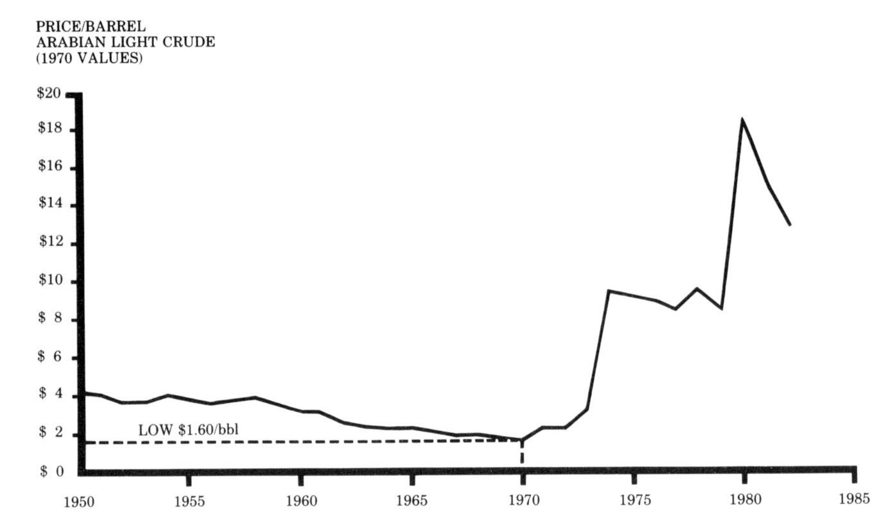

technical argument why this was impossible. By the late '60s, most OPEC members were getting tired of asking and two in particular were becoming militant – Libya and Iraq.

In September 1970 Libya could wait no longer. She broke ranks with OPEC, nationalised BP's assets and raised her posted price from $2.17 to $2.485 a barrel, to be immediately followed by Iraq. Gradually over the next months the rest of OPEC followed suit. By February 1971 all OPEC crudes had had their prices increased, not necessarily by much, some 15%, some 30%. The freeze was off.

It was as though a spell had been broken. The endless arguments by the majors over the years against any price increases were shown to be completely false. As soon as OPEC had put up its prices, all that the majors did was to pass them directly onto the consumers, who accepted them, if begrudgingly. As long as OPEC worked together, it was free to do what it wanted with prices.

Throughout 1971 and 1972 further modest price increases were negotiated. Many inconsistencies had grown into the posted price structure since it had been frozen. Some crudes needed new quality premia. Others had to have their freight premia adjusted with Suez closing in 1967; African and Mediterranean crudes had a considerable but unrecognised locational advantage relative to Gulf crudes for European and American markets.

By 1973, Persian Gulf prices had risen to around the $3.00 a barrel level, some 60-80% higher than their 1970 level. They were now around the 1960 level adjusted for inflation. There was general agreement on making further allowances for inflation and the relative competitiveness of different crudes based on quality and location. The market seemed to have rapidly restructured itself into a new type of order. However, not all members of OPEC were content with the gains made to date; the militants still felt aggrieved for the way in which the majors had held down their posted prices in the '60s. What was obvious to all was that the control over prices had very definitely shifted from the majors to OPEC. But with hindsight what was not at all obvious was that OPEC had only used this power sparingly to date.

The world did not have to wait long to see OPEC really show its new found muscle. On October 6th, 1973 the Yom Kippur war broke out. Tension between Egypt and Israel had never been relaxed since Israel had captured Sinai in 1967. Now it was Egypt's turn. She caught Israel off guard, crossed the Suez and began to recapture large tracts of the desert. However, the Israelis quickly counter-attacked and began to push Egypt back.

Most of the major powers attempted to keep out of this conflict. The Arabs, seeing their champions beginning to be beaten, put pressure on the West to support the Egyptian cause. Diplomacy got them nowhere so they turned to the "oil weapon", and it was towards the USA that they pointed it. Although the USA badly needed Arab oil, her historical links with Israel were too great to be severed. Saudi Arabia in particular was furious at the USA's intransigence. She had been led to believe by the US majors that the US was also her ally. It quickly became obvious that President Nixon was not going to halt his military aid to Israel. King Feisal turned on the USA and with vengeance. He placed an embargo firstly on all crude exports to the USA, then all refined products, whilst at the same time introducing drastic price increases.

By October 1973, Arabian Light's posted price had jumped to $5.119 a barrel, and by January 1974 to $11.651 a barrel. Only a year earlier OPEC had agreed to inflation indexing which would have put Arabian Light at $2.705 in January 1974, less than a quarter of what turned out to be reality.

In addition to all of this, eastern Mediterranean exports were severely cut back. The Arab side of OPEC, OAPEC, joined Saudi in her embargo of exports to the USA and added the Netherlands to the black list, whilst also cutting their total production by 5-10%. The West's economic boom went bust. Oil conservation measures had to be brought in by governments throughout the world, mainly aimed at the motorist, either by reducing speed limits, or banning weekend driving. By the time 1973 had turned into 1974, the tanker market was already in steep decline.

The US Government has again to take most of the blame, this time for the magnitude of the slump. Just as its action in 1959 had led to external price instability between OPEC and the majors, so it had also led to internal price instability between domestic energy consumers and producers. By shutting out

OPEC oil, it had forced US consumers to rely on US energy, but the authorities also had a large hand in controlling this. Most importantly, they had held natural gas prices down with the results that it was not economic for producers to explore for new fields. By 1970 production had begun to falter and consumers desperately looked for an alternative. The only one available in the short run was oil, but not domestic as this too was in limited supply. It therefore had to be OPEC imports.

Between 1970 and 1973, US oil imports grew from 176 to 316m tons a year, an average growth rate of 22% a year. This was all extra to the general world boom in oil and swelled demand just at the wrong time. In this short time the largest single oil market in the world turned from being domestically supplied and protected by import barriers to one desperately looking for foreign supplies. Imports grew from 25% of total US oil consumption in 1970 to 38% by 1973. Moreover, forecasts made in 1973 projected this increasing reliance on foreign oils to continue, so by 1980 some 50% of US oil would have to come abroad.

With the US oil market greater than the whole of that of Western Europe, no wonder everyone thought that demand for oil and tankers must continue to sky-rocket for the rest of the '70s. For OAPEC the USA's need for OPEC oil could not have come at a better time. For the tanker market it could not have come at a worse time. Not only did all the pundits see that this growth in seaborne oil trade would continue unabated for years to come, but also short term profits from the spot tanker market were astronomic and were all being plouged back into new tonnage.

The boom in 1970 had created spot rates of Worldscale 280 at its peak. At this level an owner received nearly $5m revenue for a single voyage from the Gulf to Europe for a 210,000-tonner. The total cost for a new ship of the same size in late 1970 was only $22m, just under what the vessel could earn in a year at peak rates. The peak in 1973 was even higher. In October spot rates hit Worldscale 350 for a single VLCC voyage from the Gulf. The cost of a new 210,000-tonner order in 1973 had risen to $45m but this could be paid for with just half a year's peak revenue.

For owners with ships free on the spot market, it was like printing money. Total voyage costs for a VLCC, including capital and operating expenses, would have been little more than Worldscale 30, leaving some 90% of revenue at the peak of the boom sheer profit. Shipowners, as with most of us, do not like paying taxes, so these profits had to be quickly reinvested, where better than shipping – so back it all went into newbuildings.

If shipowners had paid for these orders directly out of their windfall profits, the tanker world would be very different today. Fifty years ago they would probably have done just this, but the world had changed, thanks to the Norwegians and Greeks. In the '70s you did not pay for ships with cash, but credit. There was a lot of credit around.

Back in the '50s, as Japan had tried to get a foothold in the international shipbuilding scene, the Japanese Eximbank had begun offering cheap credit for export orders. European yards retaliated by forcing their governments to assist them with competitive packages. By the '60s, soft yard finance backed by government guarantees had become the norm in both Europe and Japan, which was made official in 1969 when the OECD stepped in and laid down terms for member states. In the early '70s, therefore, owners could get 80% of the cost of a new ship financed at a fixed 7½% per annum interest rate for eight years. An owner only had to put down 20% of his own money for a new ship and so the profits made in the boom of 1973 spawned far more tankers than the boom could really afford.

Added to this, commercial banks were very long in funds. Owners generally looked to a mix of yard and bank finance, preferring to be funded in dollars. Up to 1972 Japan's Eximbank would arrange dollar loans for exports, but as exchange markets became less stable they changed into Yen funding. In Europe dollar funding also became the exception and so the more astute owners looked to the international bankers to supply dollar loans in 1973. The less astute got caught very severely as exchange rates felt the backlash of the 1973 oil crisis, in particular owners who had ordered in Japan, for the Yen fell consistently until 1978.

After the Second World War, New York had been the centre for dollar finance, until 1963 when the US Government introduced a tax to stop dollars going abroad. From then on the London Euro-dollar market flourished. In the early 1970s it was given an added fillip as the US relaxed its regulations on foreign investment of pension funds and immediately more dollars were channelled into London and the Euro-dollar market.

US banks had a presence in London, but not much expertise in shipping. As the tanker market took off in 1972 they realised that they were missing out on something big and moved in to get a slice of the action. Our friendly banker was now no longer just of the old public school image in a pin-striped suit, but the US business school go-getter with a mid-Atlantic drawl. A quick scan over tanker statistics for the past five years showed him that he was onto a humdinger. Unfortunately, he probably did not look a lot further back in time and so saw all the good news since the Suez closure, but none of the bad news previous to this. Capital values had appreciated very nicely since 1967, added to which current cash flows looked healthy with spot charter rates moving upwards strongly.

Shipping departments were created overnight, and not just in London-based subsidiaries of US banks. New vice-presidents of ship finance could not wait to fund a few VLCCs. "These things are like floating real estate", he would wisely drawl over his dry martini in the bank's executive dining club, and, when he got down to the local City pub, he could be heard to boast that he'd "done another VL" and "this time, thank Christ, I got unfixed!" All they wanted to do was to lend long, sometimes as much as 20 years through special leasing deals, and buy short. A great strategy in a rising market, but not too good in a falling one.

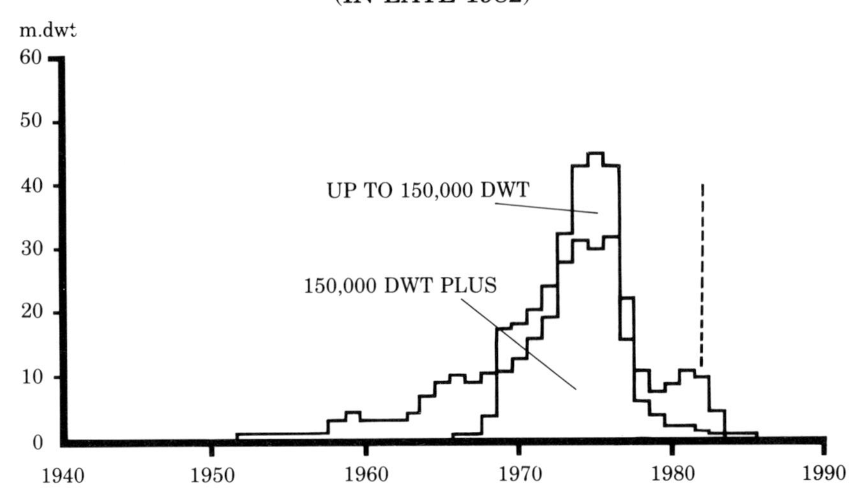

When the market collapsed in 1974 a lot of banks wished that 1973 had never happened. Gradually over the next few years their worst fears came true. Owners all round the world ran first into cash flow crises, then into pending bankruptcies. The banks tried to shore them up in rescheduling loans, or taking equity stakes in ships. But the cash crisis was too severe for many and owners went under, even leaving the banks holding the useless VLCCs.

By the mid-1970s, it was estimated that the outstanding debt on world tankers added up to some $35billion of which only some $25billion was covered by second-hand values, if they could all be sold. Many US banks had got involved, often through large funding syndicates – BankAmerica, Citicorp, Chase Manhattan, Manufacturers Hanover Trust, Morgan Guarantee, just to name a few. But it was by no means just the Americans who were exposed, British banks also took on bad risks and, in particular, the merchant bank Hambros became heavily embroiled in a number of tanker crashes, especially in Norway. However, relative to their total portfolios, these bad shipping debits were not that great and so the banks simply wrote them off, meaning that their shareholders paid.

Even now the banks blame the shipowners rather than themselves. "We only provide the funds, it's the ship owners who do the ordering", is the standard response to any implied criticism. This is true, but only part of the story. It is also a fact that few banks have permanent shipping departments. When the boom came, they created them overnight, often moving one of their middle managers rather than going outside to get someone with shipping expertise. Later when they had extracted themselves from failed shipping deals, they disbanded them just as quickly. How, therefore, could they learn from either their, or others' past mistakes and how can they put all the blame on the shoulders of the shipowner?

The independents were inevitably hit harder than the oil company tanker fleets and it was the Norwegians who were hit hardest of all. In most cases, the Greeks and Hong Kong Chinese did not over extend themselves with too many new unfixed VLCCs. Uncharacteristically, the Norwegians did. Normally they kept most of their ships in the period, not the spot market, on safe three to five year time charters. In 1972 and 1973 their timing was immaculate and many Norwegian tankers came off their old period charters at the ideal time to play the rising spot market, theoretically to be refixed onto another time charter at the height of the boom. They therefore did phenomenally well throughout 1972 and into 1973. To avoid tax they naturally looked to reinvesting their obese profits back into tankers. What went wrong was that they became over-confident. Rather than ordering one or two new ships, fixing them for a safe period then ordering some more, they just kept on ordering. The Saudi-led oil crisis in October 1973 was so sharp and severe that one moment there was mass euphoria in the tanker market, the next total dismay and the Norwegians got caught with their trousers down and most of the fleet still on the spot market.

As early as 1974 and 1975 a number of Norwegians had begun to run into serious financial problems. It was obvious that this was just the tip of a very unpleasant iceberg and that if nothing was done many important Norwegian owners would go to the wall and as a result the whole Norwegian shipping industry – owners, brokers, consultants, suppliers – could be decimated. With shipping an essential part of the Norwegian economy, the government could not idly stand by and watch this happen before its and its voters eyes. In 1976, therefore, it established the Norwegian Guarantee Institute for Ships and Drilling Vessels with 2 billion Norwegian Crowns ($380m) to prop up ailing Norwegian owners.

There was no shortage of takers. Ship after ship was refinanced via the Institute and what in reality was Norwegian Government revenue from North Sea oil. As the years moved on, it became apparent that the depression was not going to last the three to five years that had been expected. The critics became more vociferous and the government was forced to call a halt. In 1982 the Institute was closed down.

For Norway the Institute undoubtedly did a fine job. It kept the tanker industry intact and allowed it to restructure itself for the future. For the tanker world, it did a terrible job. It stopped orders from being cancelled and it stopped excess tonnage from going to the breakers. Today there are still tankers in Norwegian fiords that have never traded.

The Institute was not the only one which stopped open market forces from working to redress the balance. The international banking fraternity did the same. It saw that there could be an endemic collapse of tanker owners around the globe, a domino effect. This could increase their exposure considerably and so they stepped in to support owners where in normal times they might not have done.

Still there were terminal disasters. In Norway, the lover of the spot market, Reksten, went, to be followed by other well known names such as Hagb Waage, Fearnley & Egers and Ditlev-Simonsen. There were also Greeks who were caught out, the most famous was Minos Colocotronis who over extended himself with two very expensive 400,000-tonners. The Israeli independent, Maritime Fruit Carriers, placed a block order for 32 tankers at British yards in 1973, with disastrous consequences for both itself and the UK taxpayer who had to bail the yards out when MFC went bust.

Perhaps the most fascinating crash was that of Burmah Oil, as it epitomizes what went wrong in both tankers and oil. Burmah was one of the first to see the signs of the impending US oil import boom and announced in 1972 that it was building a VLCC transhipment terminal in the Bahamas for completion in late 1974. The idea was to offer not just trans-shipment, but an all-in transportation package from the Middle East to the US East Coast. To do this they brought in Greek shipping expertise in the form of Elias Kulukundis.

His job was to build up a fleet of tankers large enough to handle both the deepsea leg from the Gulf to the Bahamas and the shortsea leg from the Bahamas up the Atlantic Coast. He had soon long term chartered and bought some 50 tankers on the rising market, more than enough to handle the full 20 mta capacity of the Bahamas terminal and Burmah's other minor shipping requirements. When the crash came in late 1973, Kulukundis did not stop acquiring tonnage and had plans for a fleet of nearly 5m DWT by 1978. The trouble was that just as spot charter rates collapsed so did the market price of Burmah's through transportation package. It could only get the going spot market rate for its tankers which it had expensively bought or long term chartered in and was losing over $70m a year in 1974. In 1975 the whole tanker operation had to be wound up at a considerable loss to the rest of the group and the Burmah shareholders.

1973 did not only scar the independents, but also the oil companies with their own tonnage, the shipbuilders, repairers and all who had invested in the expected exponential growth for the rest of the decade.

Oil markets worldwide not only slumped but changed in structure. OPEC, not the majors, now controlled production. For BP and Gulf, this was a shock to their whole foundations. From being the largest sellers of oil in the world, they were now buyers. Alternatives to OPEC oil were researched for madly, with the new price structure of oil making many high cost production zones suddenly economic. The two new production areas were Alaska and the North Sea. Both were high cost and both needed little tanker capacity to get them to their natural markets, the US and Europe. Individual oil companies were affected to different degrees by these changes in supply and also in changes in demand as consumers around the world reacted to higher oil prices to varying degrees and not only scraped and sold tankers but also refineries.

The Seven Majors Owned Tanker Fleets 1974/82
(million DWT)

	Mid '74	*Mid '76*	*Mid '78*	*Mid '80*	*Mid '82*
BP	6.0	5.7	5.1	4.8	3.9
Chevron	7.0	8.4	9.0	9.0	8.2
Exxon	14.4	16.3	18.5	17.7	17.0
Gulf	2.5	3.1	3.8	4.1	2.8
Mobil	3.7	6.2	5.9	5.5	5.0
Shell	11.7	14.4	15.0	14.8	12.7
Texaco	5.6	7.4	7.0	6.3	5.9

The slump for shipbuilders was disastrous. They were now faced with negative orders, as owners tried to cancel, rather than the expected high growth. They tried renegotiating their orders from a tanker to, say, two smaller bulk carriers. Later, as owners realised that the flood of converted orders was ruining the dry bulk sector, they had to switch them yet again into containerships.

In anticipation of the swelling order book in the early '70s, yards had invested in new docks and expensive modern machinery. Well before the crash came, new construction and repair docks were available to handle the never-to-be-seen million-tonner. Newbuilding output was planned to triple from the 20m DWT a year in 1970 for tankers and combined carriers to around 60m DWT a year by 1975. When the bubble burst, many of these expansion plans were still only at the drawing board stage, but like tanker orders few were cancelled. It is amazing just how many shipping experts turned out to be A1 ostriches with their heads firmly stuck in the sand.

The surplus created in shipbuilding was far more permanent than in tankers. Ships rust and fall apart, concrete docks do not. Admittedly work forces can be cut back and yards even closed down, but the docks still remain, ready to be reactivated whenever demand picks up. It took until 1980 for there to be some measure of co-operation in reducing surplus capacity when both European and Japanese builders agreed officially to cut back capacity by 35%. Unofficially this had already happened as the industry's work force had been slashed from 0.6m to 0.4m through lack of orders.

In Europe, workers had just been laid off and had gone on the dole. In Japan, specific yards had been closed and workers retrained into completely new jobs – car, power plant and chemical production. On both sides of the world the process was slow and painful, but not enough to eliminate the surplus. The vicious price war continued to rage between Eastern and Western yards, only to be fanned by South Korean yards who, rather than cutting back, maintained a massive expansion programme funded by government money.

Just as the Norwegian government was forced to step in to protect its shipowning industry, so other governments had to prop up ailing yards to protect their workers from all being made redundant. Both builders and repairers turned to their governments for help. The builders sought government-backed finance to reduce the cost of their ships, so they could compete with Korea, whilst the repairers just looked for funds to cover their workers' weekly pay bills as owners slashed repairs to the bare minimum.

For the first time ever, the tanker market was no longer the freely competitive playground it had been for the past 120 years. Shipowners were being squeezed at one end by OPEC governments pushing demand down through higher prices and at the other by traditional shipowning and building governments sustaining the surplus in an attempt to keep their owners and yards solvent.

The magnitude of the surplus was, and still is, gargantuan. As all the newbuildings, ordered in 1973, were gradually delivered, tanker overcapacity rose to one third of demand. Over 100m DWT of tankers was unwanted. Then in 1979 OPEC pushed the price of oil up again and what with Alaska and North Sea oil replacing OPEC oil, tanker demand dropped from around 280m DWT to 200m by 1982, and the surplus rose to an almost unbelievable figure of 60-70% of demand.

Around half of this surplus was immediately taken up in slow steaming so as to cut bunker consumption. Bunkers jumped from around $10 a ton pre-1970 to $75 a ton by 1975, $180 by 1980 and $240 a ton at the end of 1981. The rest of this surplus went into lay up or floating oil storage. Initially it was mainly the Japanese Government that looked to idle tankers to store oil against further OPEC hikes. In 1979, they were using some 5m DWT of tankers for storage and made a handsome $300m profit on their floating oil stocks when OPEC put its prices up that year. In 1981, floating tanker storage peaked at 30m DWT, or nearly 10% of the fleet, by which time the Japanese had less than 10m DWT.

At $240 a ton bunkers were 10 to 20 times what engine designers and ship owners had planned on back in 1970. Fuel economy suddenly became an industry in itself. With tanker rates at rock bottom, owners looked at any way to cut fuel bills. By reducing speed from, say, 16 to 12 knots on a VLCC, owners could cut fuel consumption by some 28%. Engines were modified wherever possible to get optimum consumption at lower speeds and even steam units were replaced by diesels, but few owners other than the majors could afford such luxuries. More fuel efficient propellers, stern designs, hull paints and auxillary machinery meant that fuel bills could be cut by over 50%.

By 1980, everyone outside the tanker market was talking of converting to coal-fired ships. What a fuss was made of this idea. As though it were new! Few bothered to look back to see the problems that had faced the industry when it had switched the other way from coal to oil some 70 years earlier. Gradually the reality dawned on builders and owners alike that there was no global coal bunkering service and without a massive conversion of world shipping from oil to coal there never would be. So, apart from a very few specialised trades, coal-fired ships stayed firmly on the drawing boards.

Bunkers were not the only costs to increase dramatically. The oil price rises of 1973 and 1979 sent inflation shock waves through the whole of the world. For tanker owners this meant that crew wages, food and travel, spare parts, new equipment and insurance premia all escalated at far faster rates than they had expected. For those with ships on the spot market, the double squeeze of rock bottom rates and rampant cost inflation had to be crippling. For those with time charters, what had seemed profitable and secure fixtures for three to 15 years suddenly turned into nightmare losses. Owners had to slash costs time and time again and when this was not enough they had to go to their charterers cap in hand to beg for an upwards revision of the charter rate. Inevitably they never got all that they asked for and were often forced to honour these charters for their full period at a loss.

One of the last resorts open to owners in their desperate search to cut costs was to reflag. The problem was, of course, that the high cost North European and Japanese flags also had the strongest maritime unions. They fought to stop their tankers being moved to cheaper flags. They even conceded lower manning levels, but the economic pressure was too great on owners and if they were not free to reflag, tankers were simply sold off. Hong Kong owners, free to operate under FOCs, had easy pickings on the second hand market as nearly new, top quality tonnage came on the market at bargain basement prices.

Flag breakdown of world tanker fleet: 1970-1982

	1970	*1972*	*1974*	*1976*	*1978*	*1980*	*1982*
USA	6%	5%	4%	4%	4%	5%	6%
UK	14%	13%	13%	10%	9%	8%	6%
Norway	11%	11%	9%	9%	8%	7%	7%
Other W Europe	23%	22%	22%	22%	23%	23%	23%
Japan	10%	12%	12%	10%	9%	9%	9%
FOC	20%	30%	32%	34%	34%	35%	33%
Rest of world	7%	7%	8%	11%	13%	13%	16%
Total	100%	100%	100%	100%	100%	100%	100%

Source: *BP Statistical Review of World Energy*

In the 10 years from 1972 to 1982, the three largest national tanker flags – the UK, Norway and Japan – declined in importance from 36% of the total fleet to 22%, whilst FOCs and the rest of the world rose from 37% to 49%. Over 10% of the world tanker fleet had, therefore, been switched from high to low cost flags. With oil company tonnage by and large guaranteed employment in the parent company trades, it was the independent sector that took the brunt of this shift.

Yet underneath these figures a new factor was beginning to emerge. In addition to independent, oil company and government fleets a fourth sector – OPEC fleets – was evolving.

In the depressed market, one might have though that OPEC would have moved in and built up its own fleets with good second hand tonnage at bargain basement prices, but, surprisingly, not so. By 1982 OPEC members owned only some 15m DWT of tankers under their national flags, or just some 5% of the world fleet. Although the '70s had seen OPEC kick the majors out of their national oil industries and take over control themselves, their was obviously a great hesitancy amongst all OPEC members to move into assets outside their national frontiers, including tankers.

This was really rather odd, since countries like Kuwait and Saudi Arabia invested heavily in the West's stock markets and non-oil industries. Strangely, there were apparently no moves to use petro-dollars to buy into downstream oil operations, whether distribution like tankers, or market located refineries, or retail outlets such as garage chains. Instead they planned for huge expansions of oil and petrochemical processing capacity at home – in other words, source located refineries.

To Western eyes these plans were crazy. To begin with, source located refining had become uneconomic in the 1950s. It was at least 20% cheaper to ship crude oil rather than refined products, as much bigger and simpler tankers could be used, added to which Middle East refineries cost a lot more to build and run compared with market located plants in, say, Europe. Of course, with crude oil at $200 a ton, the odd dollar or two that could be saved through market located refineries was of considerably less importance than when crude was $10 a ton. Still, these odd dollars added up quickly to very large sums when one was talking of throughputs of 20m tons a year for each of these new plants.

For the oil industry, these plans were bad news, as it was plain that OPEC would try to force the world to use their growing refining capacity at the expense of plants elsewhere in the world. The surplus of world refining was, therefore, going to get worse and all become concentrated in consuming countries. For the tanker industry they initially looked liked good news since there were few tankers ideally suited to the new long haul products trades that these plants would create. In reality they also turned out to be bad news, because owners saw these trades as the only hopeful sign of a good market for years to come and quickly swamped it with far too many new ships, added to which many of these plans got badly delayed and even cancelled.

So why did OPEC not venture outside its member states in its involvement in the oil industry? It certainly had the money to do so if it wished. It would seem to have been a logical investment strategy as a means to maintain its control over competition and hence price – remember Rockefeller. OPEC clearly did not see it this way and stayed a seller of oil ex each member state's coastline.

One possible reason was security. If OPEC had assets abroad, then it would not be free to use the oil weapon whenever it wished, for the West could always retaliate and nationalise, or at least confiscate these foreign assets. But does this argument really hold water? Would the West do such a thing and could the West hold onto OPEC's investments indefinitely? Surely the answer must be no. However, back in the 1970s, OPEC certainly perceived this as a real threat: whether they do today is another matter. There is a second possible reason for OPEC not investing abroad, and that is that they were told not to by someone very powerful, so powerful that they listened. There is only one candidate for this role and that is the US Government. It is not too far fetched that the USA, on behalf of its allies in Europe and its oil companies at home, did a deal with Saudi Arabia and hence with OPEC, that OPEC could do whatever it liked in its own back yard but not abroad. Oil is still the West's jugular. It can take OPEC stopping exports, but it cannot afford OPEC controlling its refineries and retail outlets. One thing is certain and that is that Saudi Arabia is nowadays protected by US military hardware.

Perhaps, therefore, it was not surprising that one of the first tentative steps OPEC made into tankers was as an independent owner, not as an integrated oil company. AMPTC, the Arab Maritime Petroleum Transport Company, was established in 1975 and owned by OAPEC itself. By the end of 1982 it owned eight oil and two gas tankers totalling 2.2m DWT, five of the oil tankers being laid up. It paid over the odds for its ships and had to bring in expensive Europeans to manage them. At one time it even complained that it was being victimised by the majors who, it said, were purposefully not giving it charters. As an independent shipping company, it has lost its shareholders a lot of money and has taught the Arabs that running tankers is not quite the same as sailing dhows.

By the end of 1982, the largest state-owned Arab fleet was the Kuwait. The Kuwait Oil Tanker Company, KOTC, is government-owned, also with a fleet of 2.2m DWT. Iraq owned a fleet of 1.4m DWT, whilst Abu Dhabi and Algeria, 0.7m DWT each. Iran on the other hand has a fleet of 1.1m DWT, half of which are in a joint venture with BP, being ex BP tankers. All of these fleets are tiny compared with the total demand each country generates for tankers with its own exports. The largest of all OPEC tanker fleets at the end of 1982 was that of Saudi Arabia, but unlike the rest of OPEC, this was privately rather than publicly owned. A strange way to build up a national flag fleet, but one which would save any embarrassment between the Saudi ruling family and, say, the western powers. During the '70s the Saudi fleet was little more than 2m DWT, then in 1980 the Saudis introduced a 90% bunker subsidy for Saudi flag ships and by end-1982 its tanker fleet had jumped to 7m DWT.

Tanker owners looked hungrily at the immense saving that could be made under Saudi flag. Those that had set up joint Saudi companies during the '70s now cashed in. Just as BP had managed to get rid of the odd unwanted VLCC via its joint venture with Iran, so both Mobil and Texaco had similar deals going in Saudi. Mobil was involved in two Saudi companies, AIMCO and SAMARCO, whose fleets by end 82 added up to 2.4m DWT. The other major Saudi joint venture was by the Swedish independent Salen who managed to switch tankers from Swedish flag into Saudi through A/S Safina Co, which by end 1982 had a 1.2m DWT tanker fleet. Added to these there were a number of small joint ventures often done with prominent Saudi merchant princes.

Saudi Arabia was not alone in offering cheap bunkers to its national flag. Indonesia, Mexico and Venezuela all introduced similar schemes in the early '80s, but none allowed foreign tonnage to reflag into them. Saudi was the exception in more ways than one, but even so OPEC's prime interest in tankers to date is for coastal trading around member states coasts, not for deepsea trading and certainly not for integration into a global strategy of downstream expansion. If this had not been the case, then today's tanker world would be very different from what we see. However even this is beginning to change, for Kuwait has at last bought into market-located refining and retailing by acquiring all of Gulf's Dutch and Belgium assets. Perhaps this is the start of the first vertically integrated OPEC national oil company.

If the hand of OPEC was not felt directly in the market, it certainly was indirectly. The one thing that the majors have to be praised for is the superb global distribution system that they established. When OPEC took over, this was destroyed. No longer could every cargo size be perfectly matched to individual vessel capacity. No longer was cargo immediately available as soon as a tanker berthed. No longer was the right grade of oil always available. No longer were cargoes regularly exchanged between majors to optimise distribution patterns.

As a result deadfreight, multi-porting, unscheduled delays awaiting berth went up. Whilst the optimum size of tanker went down. 300,000-tonners became an embarrasment at times, let alone the handful of 500,000-tonners that had been optimistically built. New economic rules came into play. The charterer of ULCCs and even VLCCs had to balance whether to wait for another parcel of crude to top his ship up and so pay more hire costs, or sail part full and so minimise the interest costs on his valuable cargo of oil already loaded.

Some people said that the era of the supertanker was over, but this was plain rubbish. The economies of scale were still there for anyone to profit from. What had happened was that the inexorable growth in the maximum size of tanker had stopped. A new economic order had taken over, one that was less efficient, and for the first time ever that maximum size actually declined if only marginally.

MAJOR WORLD SEABORNE OIL MOVEMENTS – 1975

(Total 1390 million tons per year)

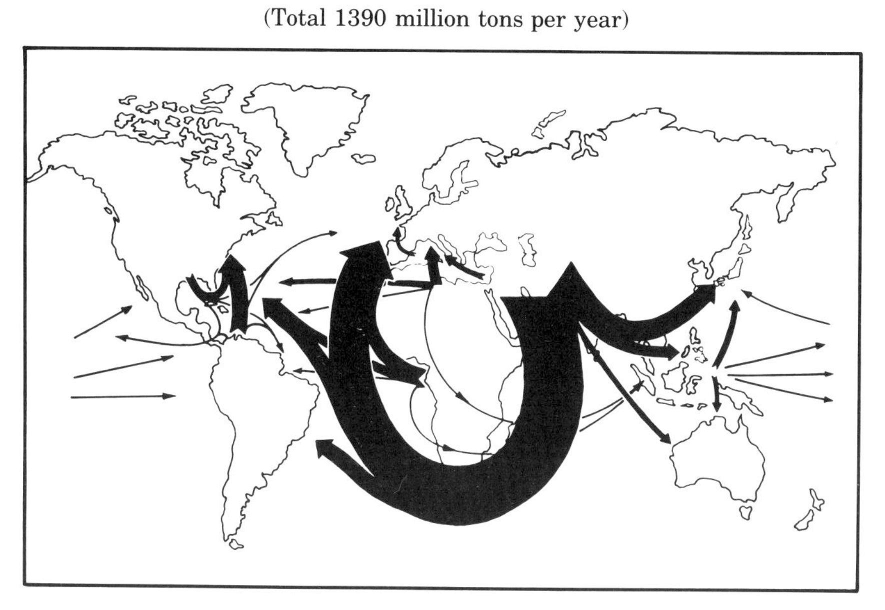

MAJOR WORLD TANKER TRADES – 1975

(Total 193 million DWT)

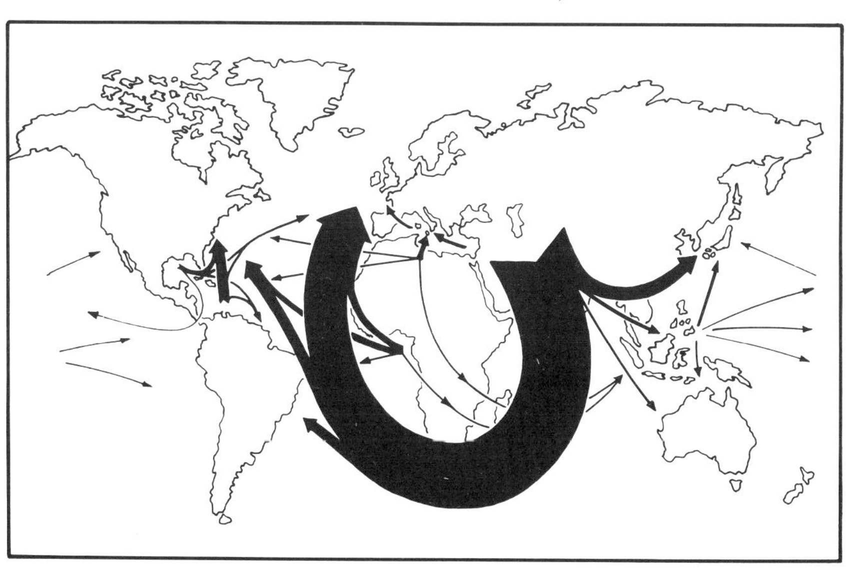

1975: Algerian Energy Minister Belaid Adbesselam (left) greets Sheikh Zaki Yamani of Saudi Arabia prior to an OPEC summit.

BOOK IV
THE CRYSTAL BALL
(1984– ?)

The Amoco Group's North West Hutton platform, positioned 300 miles north-west of Aberdeen in 1983 for the start-up of production on block 211/27.

Aerial view of British Petroleum's Isle of Grain (Kent) refinery.

19 WHERE NOW?

The 1970s were a watershed. The world economy was turned upside down and has yet to right itself properly. As the cost of energy soared with the price of oil leaping by over a factor of ten, economic growth collapsed and everyone looked at ways to conserve energy. The tanker market became a disaster. Demand melted away and by the end of 1982 over 40% of the fleet was redundant, added to which nearly all of it had been designed to run on cheap not expensive oil.

Today we can look back at these traumatic years and see just how our world has changed. We never will go back to a $1 a barrel oil or to energy markets where consumers and planners alike firmly believed that oil prices are rigidly stable, or to a world where everyone is simply waiting for the inevitable first million ton tanker to be launched.

You cannot turn the clock back. Not only has our world changed, but so has our perception of its future. We can no more believe today that the price of oil will drop by a factor of ten over the next year than we can expect to read in tomorrow's paper that the dream million tonner has just been ordered. To look into the future now, we peer through very different coloured glasses than we did 10 years ago.

From where we stand today, the outlook seems depressingly gloomy as far as one can see. How on earth is a surplus of 40% going to be got rid of? Owners doggedly refuse to scrap their ships and at the slightest upturn even order new tonnage, only to prolong the misery further.

Somehow we must stand back from today's problems to try to get a clearer vision of the future and to do this it is worth trying to see what have been the basic structural changes to the market over the past 10 years, for from these we might get a better idea of what the future holds for us.

Let us start with the basic driving force behind the market – world economic activity. Has this changed? This is not at all an easy question to answer. It is rather like bobbing up and down in a rowing boat and trying to assess if the tide has changed. There are so many short term fluctuations it is nigh impossible to see if there has been a long term structural change in the world economy.

However, when one tries to split out the long term fluctuations from the short, it is interesting that one finds a number of apparently regular "cycles" rather than just random fluctuations. If the past patterns of these cycles continue into the future, then one has a good chance of making some reasonable predictions.

So what are these "economic cycles". Apart from the obvious annual cycle due to the seasons, the best known is the "business cycle" of some three to four years. Economies cannot control themselves in periods of expansion and as they surge out of depressions they all too soon hit capacity and resource limits. Their momentum is lost, the boom peters out and they fall back into another depression to restructure and to make another dash upwards in a few years time.

A far less well accepted cycle is the 50 to 60 year, long term cycle put forward by the Russian economist Kondratieff early this century. He looked at key economic indicators for the US, England and France from back in the 18th century and believed that he saw this long term cycle. Many observers later disputed his findings saying that any regularity was more due to chance than fundamental global economic forces. The problem for Kondratieff was that even over such a long period, the number of peaks and troughs was very small and so the cycle was not proven.

He saw peaks around 1800/1810, 1860/1870 and 1910/1920 and lows around 1785/1795, 1840/1850 and 1890/1900. If his theory is right then the next peak should have occured around 1970. The post war boom up to 1973 fits very comfortably into this picture, unfortunately it also implies that there will now be a 25/30 year decline into the late 1990s before this long term cycle bottoms out and only then starts to move up strongly again.

There are insufficient data to prove today whether Kontratieff is right or wrong, but his theory has a certain appeal even if it does spell another 10 years of depression. Why should not the global economy go through long term periods of expansion and contraction, just as individual economies go through similar cycles, but of much shorter periodicity? If this is correct then we can conclude that 1973 did see a major structural change in the world economy as it peaked and moved into its downward part of the Kondratieff cycle.

The problem with this theory is that it is by no means as easy to see the forces behind it as it is with the business cycle. One of the prime reasons that it was criticised when first put forward was that its peaks coincided with wars: the Napleonic War, the US Civil War and the First World War. 1973 was, of course, the Middle East War. Is there some mysterious force creating wars every 50 years, or is it just fate? No, there must be more to it than just a convenient conjunction of astrological forces every half century, but what it *is* is not at all obvious.

What does stand out is the radical difference between the pre- and post-'73 world economy: just as though it had turned from boom to bust. From the Second World War to 1973 there was expansion and a growth of free trade, since '73 the exact reverse. Pre-'73 there were stable financial markets around the world. Post-'73 there has been financial chaos. The world financial markets have yet to stabilise from the body blows they received in 1973 and 1979 from OPEC price hikes. The effect in both years was to move, physically, billions of dollars out of oil consumer into producer economies. The financial world could not handle such radical changes overnight and as a result there was spiralling inflation followed by huge foreign exchange fluctuations in the West and massive foreign debit in Third World countries.

KONDRATIEFF'S DIAGRAM

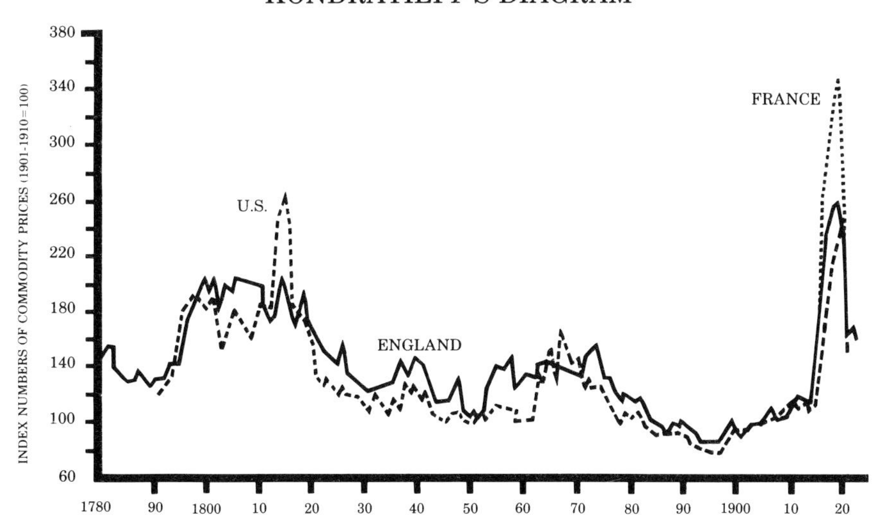

To try to get these effects under control, Western governments found themselves putting up protective barriers, which have damaged trade and hence economic activity world-wide. Today, we are still left with the residue of these events. Interest rates stolidly refuse to fall to pre-1973 levels and a number of Third World countries are virtually bankrupt, being unable to pay even the interest on the debts to world banks.

It would seem highly optimistic to see the financial world returning to normality within five years and 10 years must be nearer the mark if there is another sudden oil price rise. It is a very brave man who completely rules out any more OPEC price leaps. As with the seller of any commodity, OPEC have pushed up their prices when demand has been strong, in other words during the booms of the business cycle in 1973 and 1979. If there is another firm upturn in the cycle during the rest of the '80s why should OPEC not try to regain the losses in price that it has suffered since 1979. If this were to happen the global recovery would be put back another five years at least.

The reality of today's world is that OPEC can, and in all probability, will do just that. Even though OPEC production has fallen from a peak of some 32 million b/d to under 18 million b/d it is still powerful enough to be the key factor determining the price of world oil. Only when sufficient non-OPEC reserves have been developed, or importers have cut back, through conservation or the use of alternatives to oil, will the power of OPEC be neutralised. In the meanwhile, the world economy will remain highly sensitive to the ability to OPEC to push up oil prices, and we are not going to see a sustained period of prosperity in such an environment.

One could turn this round another way and simply state that it is ridiculous to conceive a strong world economy whilst OPEC has real power over the price of oil. It is very tempting to feed this into the Kondratieff theory and argue that the upward half of the cycle from the Second World War to 1973 was due to the exploitation of OPEC oil. The creation of OPEC was inevitable, to counteract the power of the majors, which they had built up themselves on the back of cheap oil. Similarly the destruction of the post war boom in the early '70s was also bound to come as the forces driving it had reached breaking point. Now we have to go through 25/30 years of depression for the world to overcome the power of OPEC and for some other new global force to rise like a phoenix.

This may seem a little farfetched, but there is also a grain of truth in it. It is not inconceivable that large new non-OPEC reserves will be opened up by the 1990s. The US has found unexpected new fields, both on land and off-shore. The Celtic Sea could be promising for northern Europe and the China Sea for the Far East. Perhaps then the power of OPEC is only to last for another 10 years or so, after which the world's economies can stabilise and work together for another period of sustained growth.

If this were to happen then the tanker market at the turn of the century would be a very different beast from the one it has been since the Second World War. It would revert back to its structure in the first half of this century when it was dominated by short rather than long hauls. This would have significant implications for tanker size, with a tendency towards smaller rather than bigger. It would also mean that today's surplus is not going to disappear overnight as demand may never pick up for super tankers, the prime ship type in surplus. One could see a scenario of total demand continuing to drift downwards, as less and less long haul OPEC oil is shipped apart from short

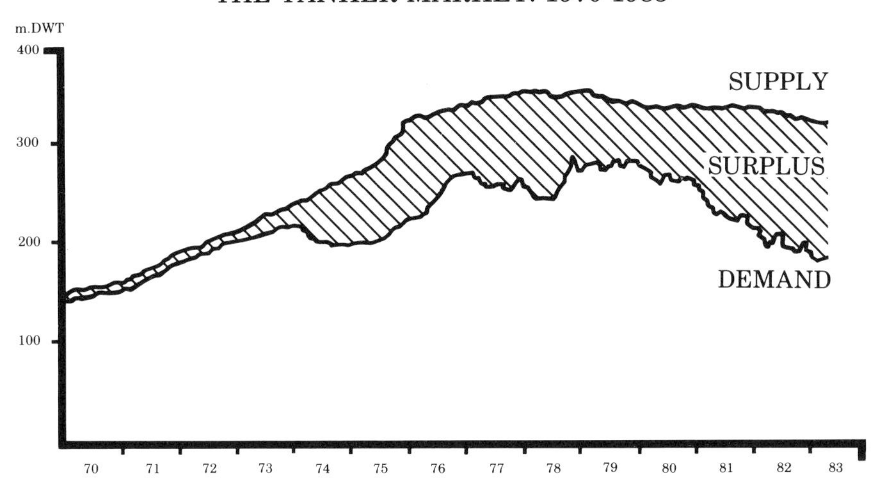

Source: Lloyd's Shipping Economist

term boosts to the moral of the market with the odd upturn in the business cycle. Gradually as the years go by, more and more VLCCs will be scrapped, but not replaced, and then as new short haul fields come on stream the demand for new tankers will be in far smaller sizes, probably no greater than 150,000 DWT.

Although it is not possible to be sure that there is even a Kondratieff cycle, let alone what the forces behind it might be, it is fun to speculate. Some observers have seen a fundamental logic to his cycle other than the war gods getting together every 50 years or so and doing a little mischief to keep themselves amused. They see the theory as a reflection of the world exploiting major technological changes, as opposed to the business cycle which exploits existing technology. For instance the economist Joseph Schumpter put the late 18th century Kondratieff upswing down to the introduction of steam power, the mid-19th century peak to the effects of the railways and the early 20th century boom to the internal combustion engine and electricity. The post Second World War upturn he accounts for with the development of chemicals, aircraft and electronics. Both chemicals and aircraft stem from oil – you cannot fuel planes on coal. However he might have been a little premature in putting electronics into the pre-'73 boom for it is only today that we are seeing the true potential of the silicon chip in micro-miniaturisation.

The one visible technological revolution that can be seen today is the effect of microcomputers sweeping through our whole existence. We play games with them at home, have them sitting on our desks in the office, they guide our aircraft and calculate our fuel consumption in our cars; the only problem is that they do not all talk to each other. That is for tomorrow. Within 10 to 20 years or even less fibre optics will have allowed all these separate machines to communicate with each other at very little cost. Why should not this be the force to pull us up into the next new global super boom?

Gazing into this crystal ball gives the same depressing outlook for tankers into the 1990s, but says little after that. The next long term boom could just as well exploit long, or short haul oil. But then, on the other hand, it may not need huge volumes of oil to power it, for it may be a boom in creating new ideas at computer terminals, rather than physically working in factories.

All of this tends to imply that the 1970s saw not only a radical structural change in the demand for tankers, but also the high point of the market from which it can now only continue to contract. Demand has already dropped from its peak in 1979 of 280m DWT to less than 200m DWT by the end of 1982 and falling. This has left a surplus of 130m DWT and with tanker scrapping at only some 20/30m per year, it would take until 1987/89 at this rate for this surplus to be eradicated, assuming no new ordering boom in the meanwhile. Ordering, thank goodness, has dropped to only some 1m DWT a year, but there is no guarantee that it will stay at this level for the rest of the decade. It is more than probable that just as the end of the surplus is in sight, owners will be tempted to rush in and buy speculative new tonnage, especially if there was an upturn in the business cycle. If this were to happen then some sort of order could not market before the mid-1990s – back to Kondratieff again?

It seems crazy, but it is true that with this diabolical oversupply we still have a situation where world banking is supporting tanker newbuilding with subsidised cheap finance. This money is being channelled to owners via the yards themselves; no wonder that owners are tempted to place new orders at the slightest opportunity if government backed cheap finance is readily available. OECD ship finance terms are still at 8½% per year interest over 8½ years for up to 80% of the capital cost. Individual governments are offering even better terms for sales to so-called "developing" country owners in the vain hope of keeping their domestic shipyards afloat a little longer than their competitor next door. While this lasts, how can stability return to the tanker market?

With the continuing prospect of declining demand, plus the threat of owners rushing to place orders at the slightest chance with the encouragement of cheap Western government finance, one must be mad to stay in the tanker market. The major oil companies have already radically changed their ownership policies. Tankers have to make money nowadays, rather than being something on which the company flag can happily wave whatever the cost. Fleets have been decimated. Ships have been sold either to breakers, or to independents with lower cost operations. To search out the least costs, tankers have been steadily drifting into Far East control and there is no reason to suppose that these trends will not continue well into the 1990s.

Even the moves by OPEC into tank ownership seem to have been halted. Perhaps a few years ago one might have been tempted to predict that OPEC could become a major force in the tanker market, but even OPEC has cash problems and can find far better areas to invest its revenues than in tankers. Like the dry bulk carrier market, the tanker market has become the province of the true independent owner, the speculator, the entrepreneur.

There are too many negative factors in the market today to make one optimistic about its future. There is the general malaise in the world's economy. There is the continuing power of OPEC in the background. There is the cheap government finance supporting a huge excess of shipbuilding capacity.

Once some of these fundamental problems can be resolved then the tanker market has a chance to restructure itself, but in the meanwhile it will just wallow from crisis to crisis.

INDEX